DO YOU REMEMBER?
THE ★ ★ ★ ★
1970s

An exclusive edition for

ALLSORTED.
for all your gift books and gift stationery

Watford, Herts, U.K. WD19 4BG

Published in 2016 by Allsorted. Watford, Herts, U.K. WD19 4BG

Compiled by Michael Powell
Illustrations reproduced courtesy of Shutterstock.com
Page 7, Marina Bolsunova: page 13, Steiner;
page 17, 360b; at Shutterstock

Concept by Milestone Design
Designed by Joanna Ross at Double Fish Design Ltd

Printed in China

*Every effort has been made to ensure the accuracy of the information contained in this book.
In the unlikely case of queries please contact the compilers via their website www.susannageoghegan.com.*

★ Introduction ★

The seventies were ace. Well, you should know because you lived through them. This special decade witnessed the first Pizza Hut, the last trolleybus and did you know that in 1973 a pint of beer cost just fourteen pence?

You could hear Marc Bolan, Baccara and Leo Sayer on the radio and watch Barbra Streisand, Richard Dreyfuss and Carrie Fisher on the big screen. Leeds United won the FA Cup, NASA sent space probes to Mars and Basil Fawlty thrashed his Austin 1100 Countryman with a tree branch. What a great time to be growing up.

Well, that was all a long time ago, but you'd be surprised how many memories you can refresh with a little encouragement. There are 54 quizzes and more than 1,000 questions covering world events, music, films, celebrities, fads and crazes, fashions, comedians, actors, singers, inventions, advertisements, novels, toys, sporting greats, scientific achievements and lots of things that made your seventies childhood unique.

Some of the questions will be easy for you to answer but almost impossible for those without your personal experience. Other questions will call up random memories to make you smile. All those real moments have disappeared but you will always have this book to remind you!

Contents

Contents

The year that was

★ 1970 ★

1. On 1st January, what happened to the age of majority in the UK?

2. Which coin ceased to be legal tender in the UK?

3. On 22nd January, which commercial airliner touched down at Heathrow Airport – the first jumbo jet to land in Britain?

4. On 26th January, which rock and roll front man was fined £200 for possession of cannabis?

5. In February, which rear-wheel drive small family car was launched by the Rootes Group to compete with the Ford Escort and Vauxhall Viva?

6. Whose eponymous debut album, released on 13th February, was the first significant heavy metal album release in the UK?

7. Which member of the British Royal Family joined the Royal Navy?

8. On 6th March, the importation of pets into the UK was banned after an outbreak of which disease in Newmarket, Suffolk?

9. On 10th April, who announced that he was leaving The Beatles?

10. On 18th April, British Leyland announced that the Morris Minor would be replaced by which larger family car?

11. On 19th May, the government bailed out which prestigious British engineering company with a £20 million loan?

12. On 24th May, The Britannia Bridge, crossing the Menai Strait in North Wales, was badly damaged by what?

13. On 28th May, which English football hero was arrested in Bogotá, Colombia, on suspicion of stealing a bracelet (and later cleared)?

14. On 13th June, who became the first actor to be given a peerage?

15. On 17th June, British Leyland launched which luxury four-wheel drive vehicle?

16. On 19th June, which party defied opinion polls by winning The General Election with a majority of 30 seats?

17. From 16th–25th July, The Commonwealth Games were held in which British city?

18. On 31st July, an issue of what was dispensed for the last time in the Royal Navy?

19. On 19th September, 1,500 people attended the debut of which British music festival?

20. What appeared in *The Sun* newspaper for the first time on 17th November?

The year that was

1971

1. On 1st January, what was speeded up in the UK, along with a removal of the requirement to find 'fault'?

2. On 3rd January, the BBC made its first broadcast for which public distance learning organisation?

3. In Egypt, which major engineering project officially opened on January 15th?

4. Which group of public sector workers began a 47-day strike on 20th January, for the first time in history, seeking a 19.5 per cent pay rise?

5. Which British luxury engineering company went bankrupt and was nationalised in February?

6. On 1st February, how did listening to the radio become a whole lot cheaper?

7. In Ontario, California on 28th February, who set a world record by jumping 19 cars on a motorcycle?

8. In April, why did eight members of the Welsh Language Society go on trial?

9. On 1st April in the UK, all restrictions were lifted on the ownership of what commodity?

10. Which trendy London store was bombed by The Angry Brigade on 1st May?

11. Which British newspaper switched from being a broadsheet to a tabloid on 2nd May?

12. Britain's oldest tabloid newspaper was discontinued after 62 years. What was its name?

13. On 7th June, which children's television programme buried a time capsule at BBC Television Centre to be opened in the year 2000?

14. In June, which British jazz and progressive music event took place for the first time?

15. Name the British Ambassador who was freed on 9th September after eight months in captivity under extreme left-wing guerrillas in Uruguay.

16. On 15th September, what did Margaret Thatcher abolish for all school children over the age of seven?

17. On 28th October, the United Kingdom became the sixth nation in the world to launch what?

18. Name the major motorway interchange north of Birmingham that opened on 10th November.

19. On 2nd December, whose yearly allowance was increased from £475,000 to £980,000?

20. What appeared on cigarette packets for the first time?

The year that was

1972

1. On 1st January, which former Nazi Stormtrooper became Secretary-General of the United Nations?

2. On 9th January, which Cunard ocean liner was destroyed by fire in Hong Kong harbour?

3. The 30th January became known as 'Bloody Sunday' when troops killed 14 demonstrators in which city in Northern Ireland?

4. On 2nd February, which building was burned down by protestors in Dublin?

5. On 9th February, a State of Emergency was declared in Britain as a result of which strike?

6. After 61 years, the last transport system of its kind in the UK ceased operation in Bradford on 26th March 1972. What was it?

7. On 22nd May, Ceylon gained independence from Great Britain and changed its name to what?

8. On 1st April, who was appointed as the first Northern Ireland Secretary?

9. From 12th May, jurors in the UK no longer had to own what?

10. On 5th June, the funeral of which former British king was held at Windsor Castle?

11. On 17th June, five White House operatives were arrested for breaking into the offices of the Democratic National Committee. Name the US national scandal that ensued.

12. On 1st July, the first official anti-discrimination rally took place in London for which civil rights movement?

13. On 6th August, which African dictator announced the expulsion from his country of 50,000 Asians with British passports?

14. On 1st September, which American beat Boris Spassky to become the World Chess Champion?

15. On 13th September, French retail giant Carrefour opened its first UK hypermarket in which town in South Wales?

16. In October, who was appointed Poet Laureate?

17. On 23rd October, a new British and Irish credit card brand was introduced to rival the already established Barclaycard. What was its name?

18. On 11th December, Eugene Cernan became the eleventh and last man to do what?

19. *The Joy of Sex* book was released, taking which 1936 bestseller by Irma S. Rombauer as its inspiration?

20. What rose above 1 million for the first time in the UK since the 1930s?

THE YEAR THAT WAS

★ 1973 ★

1. On 1st January, the United Kingdom and the Republic of Ireland entered what has since become the European Union. What was its name?

2. On 11th January, which singer performed a concert in Hawaii that was broadcast live via satellite to more than 1 billion viewers worldwide?

3. On 17th March, Queen Elizabeth II opened which prestressed concrete box girder bridge?

4. On 26th March, which international markets infrastructure business admitted women for the first time?

5. On 27th March, which Francis Ford Coppola film won the Academy Award for Best Picture?

6. On 1st April, which tax came into effect in the UK for the first time, set at 10 per cent?

7. On 8th April, which Cubist painter died at his home in France, aged 91?

8. On 3rd May, the world's tallest building was completed in Chicago. What was its name?

9. On 5th May, the BBC aired the first episode of a groundbreaking television documentary series, written and presented by Jacob Bronowski. What was its title?

10. The United States' first space station was launched on 14th May. What was it called?

11. Which national repository of information was created on 1st July 1973?

12. On 5th July, The Isle of Man Post began to issue what for the first time?

13. On 20th September in Houston, Texas, who did Billie Jean King defeat 6–4, 6–3, 6–3 in The Battle of the Sexes?

14. Which iconic stadium located in the Bronx closed on 30th September for a $160 million refurbishment?

15. Which war took place between 6th and 25th October?

16. On 8th October, Britain's first legal commercial Independent Local Radio station was launched. What was its name?

17. Which exiled spiritual leader made his first visit to the UK on 20th October?

18. Who got married in Westminster Abbey on 14th November?

19. On 30th December, the Venezuelan terrorist Ilich Ramírez Sánchez made an unsuccessful assassination attempt on British businessman Joseph Sieff. What was his nickname?

20. Which fast food chain opened its first UK restaurant in Islington, London?

The year that was

1974

1. New Year's Day was celebrated in the UK as what for the first time?

2. On 1st January, what measure was introduced by the Conservative Government to conserve electricity because of industrial action and the high price of oil?

3. How did Edward Heath's attempt to end the Miners' Strike backfire on 28th February?

4. On 6th March, how did Harold Wilson end the miners' strike?

5. In April, the United States Census Bureau estimated that the world population had reached how many billion people?

6. Name the recently founded Soviet carmaker that started selling its four-door saloon in the UK in April for £999.

7. On 5th April, Stephen King published his first novel. What was its title?

8. On 6th April in Brighton, which pop group won The 19th Eurovision Song Contest?

9. On 27th April, which English football club was relegated from the Football League First Division for the first time in its history?

10. Jon Pertwee was replaced by Tom Baker as Doctor Who in the final episode of which four-part serial?

11. What occurred at Westminster Hall in the Houses of Parliament on 17th June?

12. In July, who succeeded Alf Ramsey and caretaker England manager Joe Mercer for £200,000 a year?

13. On 12th September, who was sacked after 44 days as manager of Leeds United?

14. The BBC launched the world's first teletext information system on 23rd September. What was its name?

15. On 10th October, Harold Wilson won a second General Election with a tiny majority of how many seats?

16. The first UK McDonald's opened on 12th October in which area of Southeast London?

17. On 7th November, who disappeared following the murder of his children's nanny?

18. Why were new speed limits introduced on Britain's roads on 15th December?

19. On 22nd December, the IRA bombed the London home of which former British Prime Minister?

20. China gave two giant pandas to Britain. What were they called?

The year that was

★ **1975** ★

1. Name the iconic steel roller coaster that opened on 15th January at Walt Disney World in Florida.

2. On 11th February, Margaret Thatcher defeated Edward Heath to become leader of the Conservative Party. Which ministerial post had she held in Heath's government from 1970–74?

3. On 13th February, Britain's coal miners accepted a pay rise from the government of how much: 4 per cent, 12 per cent or 35 per cent?

4. On 28th February, 43 people were killed after a tube train on the Northern Line failed to stop at which London Underground station?

5. Which 85-year-old comedy film actor was knighted by the Queen on 4th March?

6. On 8th March, the character Davros made his first appearance in which children's programme?

7. On 9th April, Monty Python released its first film. What was its title?

8. On 1st May, Vauxhall launched the first production small hatchback in the UK. What was its name?

9. What intergovernmental organisation for the exploration of space was founded by ten member states, including the UK, on 31st May?

10. Which British cricket ground was vandalized on 19th August by supporters of the convicted armed robber, George Davis?

11. Which American president escaped an assassination attempt in Sacramento, California on 5th September?

12. The first episode of which classic sitcom was broadcast on BBC2 on 19th September?

13. On 24th September, climbers Dougal Haston and Doug Scott became the first British people to do what?

14. On 27th September, The National Railway Museum was opened in which British city?

15. On 31st October, the British rock band Queen released the most expensive single ever made at the time. What was its title?

16. Which group played its first gig at Saint Martin's School of Art on 6th November, supporting the pub rock band, Bazooka Joe?

17. Which former British motor racing champion died in a plane crash on 29th November?

18. In December, the serial killer Donald Neilson was arrested. What was his feline nickname?

19. What was the name of the fictional New England coastal resort that was terrorized by a great white shark in *Jaws*, which was released in the UK on 26th December?

20. Jackie Tabick became the UK's first female what?

The year that was

1976

1. On 21st January, the first commercial flight took place of which iconic aeroplane?

2. Who resigned as British Prime Minister on 16th March?

3. Which member of the British Royal Family announced her separation on 19th March after sixteen years of marriage?

4. Which well-connected young heiress was found guilty of armed robbery of a San Francisco bank on 20th March?

5. In Brighton, Anita Roddick opened the first what on 26th March?

6. On 1st April, which multi-billion dollar technology company was formed in Los Altos, California?

7. On 3rd April, Brotherhood of Man won The Eurovision Song Contest for the United Kingdom with which song?

8. Who became Prime Minister of the United Kingdom on 5th April?

9. On 26th June, the tallest free-standing land structure in the world opened in Toronto. What was it called?

10. Ford launched a new small three-door hatchback on 14th July. What was its name?

11. On 20th July, *Viking 1* landed successfully on which planet?

12. During the long hot summer, tens of millions of which aphid-eating insect swarmed around the UK to the delight of children?

13. On 5th August, which culturally significant mechanism located in London suffered its first and only major breakdown since it became operational in 1858?

14. The first known outbreak of which haemorrhagic viral disease occurred in Yambuku, Zaire on 26th August?

15. Which puppet based vaudeville series was broadcast for the first time on ITV on 13th September?

16. Name the new high-speed train service that was introduced in the United Kingdom on 4th October.

17. Which prominent performing arts venue opened on 25th October on London's South Bank?

18. On 1st December, which London band controversially swore several times live on Bill Grundy's early evening TV show?

19. On 3rd December, which reggae singer survived an assassination attempt in Kingston, Jamaica?

20. The Eagles released one of the best selling albums of all time on 8th December. What was its name?

THE YEAR THAT WAS

★ 1977 ★

1. James Elliot, Edward Dunham and Douglas Mink discovered the rings of which planet in our solar system?

2. Who launched a £175 pocket-sized television with a 2-inch screen on 10th January?

3. On 7th May, which world leader famously performed a pirouette behind the back of Elizabeth II?

4. On 15th May, which football team became English league champions for the tenth time?

5. Queen Elizabeth II began her Jubilee Tour of Great Britain on 17th May in which Scottish city?

6. On 27th May, Prime Minister James Callaghan officially opened which motorway, 15 years after the construction of its first stretch?

7. A gala performance for the Silver Jubilee was held on 30th May at which venue in Covent Garden?

8. Name the 26-year-old Scottish striker who became the world's most expensive footballer when he transferred from Glasgow to Liverpool FC on 10th August.

9. Which glam rock star was killed in a car crash in Barnes, London on 16th September, two weeks before his thirtieth birthday?

10. Who launched a budget airline called Skytrain on 26th September?

11. Which controversial rock group chose to mark the Silver Jubilee by performing live on a boat on the Thames on 7th June?

12. On 10th September, convicted murderer Hamida Djandoubi was the last person in France to be executed by which method?

13. Which anti-apartheid activist was killed on 12th September while in police custody?

14. On 10th October, which British music award ceremony was held for the first time?

15. On 26th October, the last natural case of which disease was diagnosed in a 23-year-old cook in Somalia?

16. Which emergency service went on strike for the first time in its history on 14th November?

17. On 15th November, the Queen became a grandmother for the first time, with whose birth?

18. On 16th December, the Queen opened a £71 million extension to the Piccadilly Line on the London Underground. What was its destination?

19. On 25th December, which Christmas Show attracted an audience of more than 28 million viewers on BBC1, one of the highest in UK television history?

20. On 27th December, the first film in a multi-billion pound franchise was released in the UK. What was its title?

The year that was

1978

1. On 13th February, who became the first female newsreader on ITV?

2. Which science-fiction comedy programme was first broadcast by BBC Radio 4 on 8th March?

3. The Conservative Party hired the advertising agency that was instrumental in winning them the election a year later. What was its name?

4. The first official what opened in the UK in April at Fairlight Glen in Covehurst Bay near Hastings?

5. Six years after Brian Clough had led Derby County to the top of the First Division, with which team did he clinch a second league win?

6. On 8th June, Naomi James became the first woman to do what?

7. Which feline cartoon strip appeared for the first time on 19th June?

8. On 19th June, which cricketer became the first person in history to score a century and take eight wickets in one innings of a Test match?

9. Which Andrew Lloyd Webber musical opened at the Prince Edward Theatre in London on 21st June?

10. Which team did Daniel Passarella captain to World Cup victory on 25th June?

11. On 25th July, who became the first person in the world to be born from in vitro fertilisation?

12. US Army Sergeant Walter Robinson took 11 hours and 30 minutes to 'walk' across which body of water using homemade water shoes on 25th August?

13. What happened to Bulgarian dissident Georgi Markov on Waterloo Bridge on 7th September, leading to his death four days later?

14. The completion of which British cathedral was officially marked by a ceremony on 25th October?

15. Name the 22-year-old Nottingham Forest defender who became the first black footballer to represent England on 29th November.

16. Which national British newspaper closed on 30th November for a year because of an industrial dispute?

17. A six-piece open-air sculpture by Canadian artist Liz Leyh went on display in Milton Keynes. What was its title?

18. To protect the earth's atmosphere, Sweden became the first country to ban what?

19. What was the biggest grossing film of the year?

20. The UK gained a new Bank Holiday on which day?

The year that was

★ 1979 ★

1. What seasonal name was given to the mass public-workers strike that began on 22nd January?

2. In New York on 2nd February, guitarist John Simon Ritchie was found dead after a heroin overdose. By what name was he better known?

3. Who became the first million pound footballer when he signed for Nottingham Forest on 9th February?

4. What did the Sahara Desert experience for 30 minutes on 18th February?

5. On 28th March, a nuclear meltdown occurred at a reactor in Pennsylvania, USA. What was its location?

6. On 28th March, a General Election was triggered when Labour Prime Minister James Callaghan lost a confidence motion in the House of Commons by how many votes?

7. Name the Conservative Northern Ireland spokesman who was killed by an IRA bomb in the House of Commons car park on 30th March.

8. On 20th April, American President Jimmy Carter was confronted by what kind of swimming creature while fishing

in his hometown of Plains, Georgia USA?

9. On 8th May, which former leader of the Liberal Party went on trial at the Old Bailey for attempted murder?

10. What menu item did the fast food chain McDonald's introduce in June?

11. In the first Conservative budget since the General Election, Chancellor Geoffrey Howe cut the standard rate of tax by 3 per cent on 12th June. By how much did he cut the top rate of 83 per cent?

12. What began its return to Earth on 11th July after spending 74 months in orbit?

13. On 17th July, which British athlete set a new World Record for the mile of 3 minutes and 48.95 seconds?

14. In August, 15 people died and dozens of yachts were destroyed by a storm in the Irish Sea during which biennial yacht race?

15. On 1st September, Pioneer 11 became the first spacecraft to fly past which planet?

16. On 11th November, the last episode of the first series of which BBC1 sitcom broke UK viewing figures for a recorded programme with 23.95 million viewers?

17. Vauxhall launched its first ever front-wheel drive car range on 14th November. What was it called?

18. Worldwide per capita production of which natural resource reached an historic peak in 1979?

19. Which South Asian country did the USSR invade in December?

20. Pope John Paul II became the first Pope to visit a Communist country. Which country did he visit?

70s Sitcoms

Name the Seventies Sitcoms that Featured the Following Cast:

LONDON

1. Yootha Joyce, Brian Murphy, Norman Eshley, Sheila Fearn, Nicholas Bond-Owen

2. Diane Keen, David Roper, Lewis Collins, Ian Saynor, Clare Kelly, John McKelvey

3. Leonard Rossiter, Frances de la Tour, Richard Beckinsale, Don Warrington

4. Eric Sykes, Hattie Jacques, Deryck Guyler, Richard Wattis

5. Polly James, Pauline Collins, Nerys Hughes, Elizabeth Estensen, Mollie Sugden

6. Michael Bates, George Layton, Windsor Davies, Melvyn Hayes, Don Estelle, Donald Hewlett, Michael Knowles

7. Trevor Bannister, Mollie Sugden, Frank Thornton, Arthur Brough, James Hayter, Alfie Bass, John Inman, Wendy Richard

8. Robert Lindsay, Cheryl Hall, Mike Grady, Hilda Braid, Anthony Millan, Peter Vaughan

9. Reg Varney, Bob Grant, Stephen Lewis, Anna Karen, Cicely Courtneidge, Doris Hare

10. Ronnie Barker, David Jason, Lynda Baron

11. Richard O'Sullivan, Paula Wilcox, Sally Thomsett, Yootha Joyce, Brian Murphy

12. Michael Crawford, Michele Dotrice, Jessica Forte

13. Leonard Rossiter, Pauline Yates, John Barron, Sue Nicholls, John Horsley

14. Wendy Craig, Geoffrey Palmer, Bruce Montague, Nicholas Lyndhurst, Andrew Hall

15. Elaine Stritch, Donald Sinden

16. Terry Scott, June Whitfield, Beryl Cooke

17. John Alderton, Deryck Guyler, Noel Howlett, Joan Sanderson, Richard Davies, Jill Kerman

18. Arthur Lowe, John Le Mesurier, Clive Dunn, John Laurie, Arnold Ridley, Ian Lavender, James Beck, Bill Pertwee

19. Bill Maynard, Megs Jenkins, Robert Keegan, Ray Mort, Richard Davies

20. James Bolam, Rodney Bewes, Brigit Forsyth, Sheila Fearn, Bill Owen

Advertising

1. Which cuddly sitcom actor used to advertise Cadbury's Curly Wurly on television?

2. What drink was advertised with the slogan 'Watch out, there's a Humphrey about'?

3. Which radio DJ voiced the meowing cat in the cut-out animated cartoon public information series *Charlie Says*?

4. Which British comic was sold with the slogan, 'Two comics in one, double the fun!'?

5. Which aftershave did British heavyweight boxer Henry Cooper advertise on television?

6. 'A man's gotta chew what a man's gotta chew'. Chew what?

7. Originally called Opal Mints, these chewy white squares had three green peppermint stripes. How were they renamed in 1976?

8. What had 'a hazelnut in every bite'?

9. Which one of these flavours would not be found in a packet of Spangles: strawberry, blackcurrant, banana, pineapple, lemon and lime?

10. Which actress played Melissa in a series of ten Cinzano adverts and always ended up with a spilt drink?

11. What did the 1979 jingle 'Get busy with the fizzy' encourage everyone to buy?

12. What popular packet-mix mousse claimed to offer 'the taste of strawberries and cream' and instructed you to 'just add milk and whisk'?

13. Complete the slogan: 'Happiness is a_____'.

14. Which drink was advertised by the catchphrase, 'No, Luton Airport'?

15. The actor Gary Myers who played Captain Lew Waterman on Gerry Anderson's cult TV series *UFO* also appeared in a long-running series of adverts for which box of chocolates?

16. What did the blond-haired seven-year-old John Cornelius begin advertising from 1974, dressed as a cowboy?

17. Which product was advertised by the song 'I Can't Let Maggie Go' by late-sixties pop group The Honeybus, with the opening words, 'She flies like a bird in the sky'?

18. Which product featured 13-year-old Carl Barlow pushing a bike up Gold Hill in Shaftesbury, Dorset?

19. Name the English film director who directed this advert.

20. With which drink do you associate the slogan: 'I'd like to teach the world to sing'?

Seventies

Sport 1

1. On 8th March 1971, the 'Fight of the Century' at Madison Square Garden was the first time that two undefeated boxers fought for the heavyweight title. Who were they and who won?

2. On 14th June 1970, England's defence of the FIFA World Cup ended when they lost 3–2 to which country in the quarter final in Mexico?

3. On 8th May 1971, which team beat Liverpool 2–1 in the FA Cup final at Wembley Stadium to become only the second English team in the century to complete the double?

4. The first what was played on 5th January 1971 between Australia and England at the Melbourne Cricket Ground?

5. On 6th August 1971, Scottish yachtsman Chay Blyth completed his round the world trip. What was unusual about his voyage?

6. In 1975, Anatoly Karpov became world chess champion by default when who failed to defend his title?

7. What was significant about South Africa's 4–0 series whitewash over Australia at Port Elizabeth on 4th March 1970?

8. What was the name of the third and final bout between Muhammad Ali and Joe Frazier on 1st October 1975?

9. In the 1975 World Series, who hit a legendary walk off home run for the Boston Red Sox at the bottom of the 12th inning to take the championship to a seventh game decider?

10. In which year during the seventies did Cambridge sink in the Boat Race?

11. In 1978, Martina Navratilova won the first of nine singles titles at Wimbledon. What was her country of birth?

12. In which year did Red Rum achieve his record-breaking third Grand National win?

13. Name the Belarusian gymnast who won three gold medals and one silver at the 1972 Munich Olympics.

14. Who won the gold medal in the Shot Put in the 1974 and 1978 Commonwealth Games and also won the inaugural Britain's Strongest Man in 1979?

15. Who officially opened the 1976 Summer Olympics in Montreal, Canada?

16. Name the 1968 Olympic champion in the 400 metres hurdles who won the first ever British Superstars competition, held in 1973.

17. Which British boxer won the WBC Light Heavyweight title in October 1974 by defeating Jorge Ahumada?

18. Which severely injured basketball player famously scored the first two baskets of Game 7 for the New York Knicks on 8th May 1970 and galvanised them to capture their first NBA Championship?

19. Name the British athlete who beat Germany's Heide Rosendahl by just 10 points to win heptathlon gold in the 1972 Olympic Games.

20. Name the Thoroughbred racehorse who, on 9th June 1973, became the first US Triple Crown (Kentucky Derby, Preakness Stakes, and Belmont Stakes) winner in 25 years.

Toys and
Games

1. Which doll, popular in the seventies, was created in 1959 by a Danish fisherman and woodcutter because he couldn't afford a Christmas gift for his young daughter?

2. Latch hook rug kits were popular with boys and girls during the seventies. What was the most popular brand?

3. Which toy consisted of two plastic robot figures fighting in a boxing ring?

4. Which educational toy, manufactured by Texas Instruments, used the first single-chip voice synthesizer, the TMC0280?

5. What code-breaking 'game of logic and cunning for two players' featured on its black rectangular box a woman wearing a white dress standing behind a seated bearded man wearing a suit?

6. What colour was the flight suit worn by the Steve Austin action figure?

7. Which mechanical drawing toy popular during the seventies was invented by André Cassagnes in the late fifties?

8. What was the name of the pattern drawing system consisting of a series of interlocking plastic cogs and toothed rings of different sizes?

9. What was the name of the doll who sat at a desk holding a pen, replicating whatever was drawn or written by the person on the other side?

10. Name the board game manufactured by Peter Pan Playthings of Peterborough that used a central Pop-O-Matic bubble to operate the die.

11. In which pirate game, sold in Britain by Waddingtons, were diamonds and rubies worth 5 points; gold 4 points; pearls 3 points and rum 2 points?

12. Which battery-operated medical game of dexterity did John Spinello sell to the Milton Bradley Company for just $500?

13. In which game did players co-operate to build a Rube Goldberg-style contraption to capture each other's mouse-shaped game pieces?

14. Which table-top football game took its name from the Latin for a small falcon commonly known as The Eurasian Hobby?

15. What was the name of the futuristic programmable utility vehicle with a keypad on top released by the Milton Bradley Company in 1979?

16. During the seventies, which toy received three innovations: lifelike hair, gripping hands and 'eagle eyes'?

17. Which iconic seventies toy was inspired by seeing children playing on a floating buoy in a Norwegian quay?

18. Name the toy that featured two battered plastic cars that fell apart after a head-on collision?

19. The object of which beat-the-clock game was to fit 25 plastic yellow shapes into their corresponding holes before the time expired and the board ejected all the pieces?

20. What was the name of the electronic games machine that looked like a red futuristic telephone and offered six games including Three-in-a-row, Blackjack 13 and Secret Number?

SEVENTIES

★ Cars ★

1. Which Ford model was the best-selling car of the early seventies?

2. Which small family car was designed to replace the long-running Ford Anglia?

3. The third most popular car of the seventies was built by British Leyland to rival the Cortina. Richard Hammond once described it as a 'drab, dreary, entirely beige, wilfully awful pile of misery'. What was its name?

4. Which little car saw a boost in sales after the energy crisis of 1973?

5. The third generation HC series of which model was the last passenger car built solely by Vauxhall?

34

6. What was the name of the first mass-produced car with an aluminium engine block and cylinder head?

7. Launched in 1973, what quickly earned the nickname 'flying pig' due to its distended styling and because it seemed to sum up everything that was wrong with British Leyland?

8. Name the large executive car that was manufactured by Ford from 1972.

9. What was the name of the wedge-shaped sports car launched by Lotus in 1976?

10. The UK's first sports coupé was marketed as 'The car you always promised yourself.' What was its name?

11. What was distinctive about the exterior of the Morris Minor 1000 Traveller?

12. Which rear-wheel drive small family car, launched in 1970, began life as a Hillman; became a Chrylser in 1976 and was rebranded as a Talbot three years later?

13. What was the van version of the Vauxhall Viva called?

14. What make of Rolls Royce was presented to Queen Elizabeth II in 1977 as her 'Silver Jubilee Car'?

15. When did the Austin 1100 and 1300 cease production?

16. Basil Fawlty thrashed his car with a tree branch in the 'Gourmet Night' episode of *Fawlty Towers*. What make was it?

17. What was the name of Hillman's compact economy car which ceased production in 1976?

18. What was the name of the razor-sharp wedge with scissor doors launched by Lamborghini in 1971?

19. In *The Spy Who Loved Me* (1977), James Bond's sports car turned into a submarine. What make was it?

20. Launched in 1976, which Aston Martin was the first car to use a digital dashboard?

Children's Television

Programmes

1. Michael Rodd was the original host of which popular children's quiz show?

2. In which programme would you hear the phrase 'All aboard the skylark'?

3. In *Chorlton and the Wheelies*, what was the name of the talking book?

4. The Gruesome Twosome, Peter Perfect and The Ant Hill Mob appeared in which high speed Hanna-Barbera cartoon?

5. Which children's programme began with the words, 'Here is a box, a musical box, wound up and ready to play. But this box can hide a secret inside. Can you guess what is in it today?'

6. In *The Muppet Show*, the two cynical old men who always heckled from their balcony seats were named after which two New York City hotels?

CHILDREN'S TELEVISION PROGRAMMES

7. Actress Emma Thompson's father wrote and narrated which long-running animated children's TV series?

8. Who had a sidekick puppet called Spit the Dog?

9. Which famous Volkswagen had the number plate OFP 857?

10. Madame Cholet was one of the Wombles. What was her job?

11. On *Pipkins*, what distinctive British accent did Pig have?

12. What was the name of the first Blue Peter pet?

13. In which children's Gerry Anderson's Supermarionation series would you find a 'Brain Impulse Galvanoscope Record & Transfer' (BIGRAT)?

14. Which planet-dwelling puppets lived on Blue String Pudding and Green Soup?

15. In the children's television series *Hector's House*, what animals were Hector, ZaZa and Kiki?

16. In which children's television programme would you find Fleegle the beagle, Bingo the gorilla, Drooper the lion and Snorky the elephant?

17. Who was the original host of the ITV children's game show, *Runaround*?

18. Which stop-motion animation series always began with the words, 'Here is the clock, the _____clock. Telling the time, steadily, sensibly; never too quickly, never too slowly. Telling the time for _____?'

19. What was the full title of the summer school holiday programme *Why Don't You*, which began on 20th August 1973 and ran for 42 series and 22 years?

20. Which programme featured 'a saggy, old cloth cat, baggy, and a bit loose at the seams'?

Seventies

★ Fashion ★

1. In the mid-seventies, *Newsweek* declared Diane Von Furstenberg the 'most marketable designer since Coco Chanel' for her invention of which dress style?

2. Who invented the jersey halter dress: Roy Halston, Elizabeth Taylor or Andy Warhol?

3. Which seventies 'look' was summed up by its creator Barbara Hulanicki as 'fresh little foals with long legs, bright faces and round dolly eyes'?

4. Which clothing chain specialising in Romantic English designs opened its first shop at 35 Maengwyn Street, Machynlleth, Montgomeryshire?

5. A 1976 poster that showed a woman smiling in a red swimsuit sold more than 12 million copies and became the best-selling pinup poster of all time. What was her name?

6. How did the crazy, sparkly outfits worn on stage by Swedish super group ABBA, save money?

7. Which ubiquitous seventies fabric derives its name from the French *serge de Nîmes*?

8. Name the French fashion designer known as the 'Queen of Knitwear'.

9. Who opened a boutique initially called 'Too Fast To Live, Too Young To Die' on London's Kings Road in 1971?

10. When Bianca Pérez-Mora Macias married Rolling Stone Mick Jagger in 1971 who designed her wedding outfit: Gloria Vanderbilt, Ossie Clark or Yves St Laurent?

11. Who popularised polo necks, beanies and knee-high boots after her portrayal of Jenny Cavalleri in 1970's tearjerker *Love Story*?

12. Which half Japanese, half American fashion icon was one of the most in-demand models of the decade?

13. Fringed shawls, denim, chiffon, lace and cowboy boots were synonymous with which Fleetwood Mac alumnus?

14. Avant-garde designer Kensai Yamamoto was responsible for many of the glam rock outfits for which David Bowie alter ego?

15. Which American supermodel and face of Revlon appeared on the front cover of *Vogue* magazine a record 41 times?

16. Film star John Travolta wore a white 3-piece suit in the 1977 blockbuster *Saturday Night Fever*. What colour was his shirt?

17. Which Italian fashion designer was responsible for popularizing the wearing of corduroy fabrics during the seventies?

18. The colourful knitwear designs of which high-end Italian fashion house peaked in the seventies?

19. Who wrote and recorded the song 'Who the Hell is Sonia Rykiel?'

20. Which Somalian supermodel was discovered by the American artist and photographer, Peter Beard, in 1975 while still at university reading political science?

Monty Python's
Flying Circus

1. What was the name of the Python theme tune and who wrote it?

2. In the Cheese Shop Sketch, what was the first cheese that John Cleese requested?

3. How much did the Argument Clinic charge for a five-minute argument?

4. What lessons did Terry Jones offer in the Argument Clinic sketch?

5. In the Spam Sketch, what other food item was on the menu apart from spam, bacon, eggs, baked beans and sausage?

6. What was the chief weapon of The Spanish Inquisition?

7. Ron Obvious of Neap's End hoped to become the first man to do what?

8. Who co-directed *Monty Python and the Holy Grail*?

9. What was the name of the Roman character played by Graham Chapman in *Monty Python's Life of Brian*?

10. In 'Bruces' Philosophers Song' who was 'a boozy beggar who could drink you under the table'?

11. What was the name of the Pythons' fourth record, released in 1973?

12. Which two English rock groups provided most of the funding to

make *Monty Python and the Holy Grail?*

13. Which former Beatle provided the $4 million budget to film *Monty Python's Life of Brian?*

14. Which sketch begins with the words, 'Hello, I'd like to register a complaint'?

15. Which two Pythons starred in the Nudge Nudge Sketch?

16. What was the name of Michael Palin's character in The Lumberjack Song Sketch?

17. What was the name of the Python book first published in 1971?

18. What was the name of John Cleese's pet halibut in the Fish License Sketch?

19. Complete this sentence: 'And now for something _____.'

20. The name of which tree often followed that sentence?

Name the actor in both

1. *The Godfather* (1972), *The Eagle Has Landed* (1976)

2. *American Graffiti* (1973), *Star Wars* (1977)

3. *Jaws* (1975), *Sorcerer* (1977)

4. *Love Story* (1970), *Paper Moon* (1973)

5. *The Last Movie* (1971), *Dirty Mary Crazy Larry* (1974)

6. *The Eiger Sanction* (1975), *Escape from Alcatraz* (1979)

7. *Cabaret* (1972), *Logan's Run* (1976)

8. *Rocky* (1976), *F.I.S.T.* (1978)

9. *The Godfather* (1972), *Rollerball* (1975)

10. *Carrie* (1976), *Grease* (1978)

11. *The Last Picture Show* (1971), *Thunderbolt and Lightfoot* (1974)

12. *Serpico* (1973), *Dog Day Afternoon* (1975)

13. *Everything You Always Wanted to Know About Sex * But Were Afraid to Ask* (1972), *Smokey and the Bandit* (1977)

14. *Straw Dogs* (1971), *All the President's Men* (1976)

15. *Don't Look Now* (1973), *Invasion of the Body Snatchers* (1978)

16. *Chinatown* (1974), *The Last Tycoon* (1976)

17. *Midnight Express* (1978), *Alien* (1979)

18. *Mean Streets* (1973), *The Deer Hunter* (1978)

NAME THE ACTOR IN BOTH FILMS

19. *Diamonds Are Forever (1971), Zardoz (1974)*

20. *The Great Gatsby (1974), All the President's Men (1976)*

21. *Annie Hall (1977), The Deer Hunter (1978)*

22. *The Cassandra Crossing (1976), Apocalypse Now (1979)*

23. *The Sting (1973), Jaws (1975)*

24. *The French Connection (1971), The Poseidon Adventure (1972)*

25. *Sleeper (1973), Annie Hall (1977)*

26. *The Godfather (1972), Superman (1978)*

27. *Capricorn One (1978), Escape to Athena (1979)*

28. *American Graffiti (1973), Jaws (1975)*

29. *Willy Wonka & the Chocolate Factory (1971), Young Frankenstein (1974)*

30. *Get Carter (1971), The Eagle Has Landed (1976)*

Robert
De Niro

1. In which year was he born?

2. De Niro's parents divorced when he was three after his father, an abstract expressionist painter, announced what?

3. What childhood nickname did his pale complexion earn him?

4. What role did he play in a school production of *The Wizard Of Oz*?

5. Between the ages of 18 and 21 he studied under which American actress and acclaimed acting teacher?

6. He played drug-addicted Lloyd Barker in the low-budget 1970 film, *Bloody Mama*. Who played his machine gun toting mother, Ma Barker?

7. Brian De Palma directed him in which 1970 film?

8. Name the three films, directed by Martin Scorsese and released during the seventies, in which De Niro starred.

9. In 1973, he played a dying sportsman in *Bang the Drum Slowly*. Which sport?

10. Which film has De Niro described as 'my feminist film . . . because it takes macho to its logical conclusion'?

11. He married his first wife in 1976. What was her name?

12. He was turned down for which role in *The Godfather*?

13. He won the Academy Award for Best Supporting Actor for which role in *The Godfather Part II*?

14. In which film did he play steelworker Michael 'Mike' Vronsky?

15. Immediately after *The Godfather Part II*, De Niro could command

$500,000 per film, but which film did he agree to make for $35,000?

16. During filming of *The Deer Hunter*, what did Christopher Walken do that nearly caused De Niro to walk off set with rage?

17. Which famous improvised line in *Taxi Driver* was copied from watching Bruce Springsteen perform in Greenwich Village?

18. For which film did he learn to play the saxophone?

19. Which Brooklyn-born actor co-starred with De Niro in *Mean Streets*?

20. Who died a few hours after completing the recording sessions for his score for *Taxi Driver* and was posthumously nominated for an Academy Award?

★ Science ★

1. In the US on 4th April, 1972 the Pulsar was launched for a retail price of $2,100 (about two thirds the price of an average car). It was the first commercially available what?

2. In which year did NASA launch *Apollo 13*?

3. In November 1971, the Intel 4004 was launched; it was the first commercial fully integrated and general purpose programmable what?

4. On 12th August 1977, the first space shuttle flew on its own for the first time. What was its name?

5. In 1976, which founder member of Apple sold his ten per cent stake in the company (shares worth approximately US$65 billion today) for US$800?

6. In 1976, Cray Research, Inc. introduced the Cray-1, the world's first what?

7. Produced from 1972 to 1981, by what name is the SX-70 folding single lens reflex Land camera better known?

8. Which obsolete videocassette magnetic tape recording format was named after the shape made by the tape as it ran through the recording heads?

9. Len Deighton's Second World War historical novel *Bomber*, published in 1970, was the first novel written on what?

10. Unix time began at 00:00:00 UTC, on 1st January in which year?

11. In 1971, Ray Tomlinson sent the first ARPAnet e-mail with the first use of which sign in an address?

12. Which infectious viral disease was eradicated from the Americas in 1971?

13. In May 1972, Magnavox released the Magnavox Odyssey – the first what of its kind that could be connected to a television set?

14. The first video game was released by Atari Incorporated in November 1972. What was its name?

15. In 1972, James Lovelock made the first reference in print to which famous ecological hypothesis?

16. In 1972, which American company launched the first scientific handheld calculator at a price of $795?

17. On 29th March 1974, NASA's Mariner 10 became the first space probe to reach which planet?

18. On 3rd December 1973, the space probe Pioneer 10 sent back the first close-up images of which planet?

19. The SETI radio survey was launched on 7th December 1973 at the Ohio State University Radio Observatory. What does SETI stand for?

20. Name the 1973 science-fiction adventure starring Yul Brynner and Richard Benjamin, the first feature film to use digital image processing.

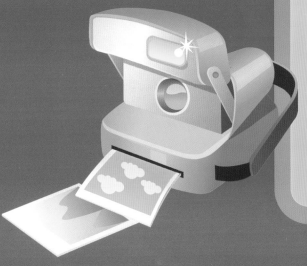

Books of the Seventies

Science Fiction

1. Name Larry Niven's classic 1970 novel set in a universe referred to as 'Known Space'.

2. Name Jack Finney's 1970 time-travelling novel in which the action zips back in time from 1970 to New York City in 1882.

3. What is the title of Ursula K. Le Guin's 1971 novel about a draftsman named George Orr, whose dreams alter reality.

4. Name Anne Mccaffrey's 1971 novel, featuring the time-travelling, dragon-riding Oldtimers.

5. What is the title of Issac Asimov's 1972 novel about an alien race who live in a parallel universe.

6. Name Ira Levin's 1972 novel about a photographer called Joanna Eberhart who leaves New York City for a small town in Connecticut inhabited by men with impossibly beautiful wives.

7. Name George Alec Effinger's 1972 novel about Seyt, his siblings and his parents, named Our Mother and Our Father, the first settlers on planet Home.

8. What is the title of Thomas Pynchon's lengthy 1973 science-fiction novel about the V-2 rocket production in Germany at the end of the Second World War.

9. Name Arthur C. Clarke's 1973 novel about a giant, cylindrical alien spaceship circling the Earth in 2130.

10. Name David Gerrold's 1973 novel about the psychological impact of time travel.

11. Which acclaimed science-fiction novel, set in 3017, was co-written by Larry Niven and Jerry Pournelle in 1974?

12. Which Ursula K. Le Guin novel, written in 1974, was set in the same fictional universe as her 1969 novel, *The Left Hand of Darkness*?

13. In which 1975 science-fiction novel does Joe Haldeman describe an interstellar war between Man and an alien race called the Taurans?

14. Which 1976 novel was the third in a series of six written by Frank Herbert, described as the best-selling science-fiction series in history?

15. Which Philip K. Dick novel, written in 1977, described the dystopian, drug-addled future of Orange County, California?

16. Which 1978 Frederik Pohl novel was set in a space station built into a hollow asteroid?

17. Which 1979 novel by Douglas Adams was the first in a series of five adapted from a radio programme of the same name?

18. Which Arthur C. Clarke novel, published in 1979, described a 22nd Century space elevator linking the Earth with an orbital satellite?

19. Which 1979 novel took a 20th-century Californian woman back to a 19th-century slave plantation in Maryland?

20. Which 1979 novel by John Varley centred on a NASA space ship commanded by Cirocco Jones and an encounter with a strange satellite of Saturn?

Opening Lines – Name that

Tune

1. 'A teenage dream's so hard to beat.'

2. 'Once I had a love and it was a gas.'

3. 'Stuck inside these four walls, sent inside forever.'

4. 'It's a God-awful small affair.'

5. 'I can't seem to face up to the facts.'

6. 'In the day we sweat it out on the streets of a runaway American dream.'

7. 'I've been really tryin', baby, tryin' to hold back these feeling for so long.'

8. 'God save the queen, the fascist regime.'

9. 'Radio, live transmission.'

10. 'You know, I was, I was wondering, you know, if you could keep on.'

11. 'Hey ho, let's go Hey ho, let's go. They're forming in a straight line.'

12. 'There's a lady who's sure all that glitters is gold.'

13. 'Loving you isn't the right thing to do.'

14. 'Very superstitious, writings on the wall.'

15. 'It's cold outside and the paint's peeling off of my walls.'

16. 'London calling to the faraway towns.'

17. 'Hello, is there anybody in there?'

18. 'Livin' easy, lovin' free, season ticket on a one way ride.'

19. 'Ooh, it's so good, it's so good, it's so good, it's so good.'

20. 'I, I will be king, and you, you will be queen.'

More Television

1. Which television comedian ended his show with the words, 'Thank you, goodnight and may your God go with you'?

2. Name the BBC television drama series that launched in September 1976 in which Gemma Jones played the eponymous Duchess.

3. What was the name of the sporty strongman Womble?

4. Which two children's programmes used a 'Gallery Theme' called 'Left Bank Two' while displaying artwork sent in by viewers?

5. What four-word phrase did impressionist Mike Yarwood always use to introduce his closing song?

6. 'Galloping Home', written by Denis King, was the theme tune for which 26-episode children's series?

7. What was the name of the Gambian-born African slave who was the lead character in the 1977 mini-series *Roots*?

8. Which sketch comedian submitted many of his script ideas to the producers of his show under the pseudonym of Gerald Wiley so they would be judged impartially?

9. What was the name of Joanna Lumley's character in *The New Avengers*?

10. What was the catchphrase of Dick Emery's busty peroxide blonde character, Mandy?

11. Name the long-running comedy series that used a saxophone tune called 'Yakety Sax' to accompany its slapstick chase scenes.

12. Which long-running BBC television sitcom was originally going to be called *The Fighting Tigers*?

13. Which maritime BBC drama series was named after screenwriter Cyril Abraham rearranged the letters of the mythological sea nymph, Ondine?

14. Actor John Forsythe played Blake Carrington on the eighties soap opera *Dynasty*, but his voice was already famous because of which glamorous seventies Los Angeles private detective series?

15. During the summer of which year did Jon Pertwee as Doctor Who regenerate into his fourth incarnation, played by Tom Baker?

16. In which programme did Nancy Kominsky star?

17. Which American TV cops had the call sign 'Zebra Three'?

18. Ronnie Barker and Norman Wisdom were the BBC's first and second choices for the lead in which BBC television sitcom that launched on 15th February 1973?

19. Which show used the theme tune 'Bean Bag' by Herb Alpert and the Tijuana Brass?

20. Barry Norman, Eddie Waring and which other sports presenter performed a memorable song and dance routine dressed in sailor's outfits on *The Morecambe and Wise Christmas Show* in 1977?

Seventies

★ Sport 2 ★

1. Name the 19-year-old Aboriginal tennis player who won the Women's Singles title at Wimbledon in 1971.

2. In 1972, who won the FA Cup for the first time with a 1–0 victory over Arsenal at Wembley Stadium?

3. Which player, who scored a goal for England in the 1966 World Cup final, became the first £200,000 footballer when he joined Tottenham Hotspur on 17th March 1970?

4. On 4th May 1974, which team won the FA Cup for the second time, beating Newcastle United 3–0 in the Wembley final?

5. On 15th August 1971, which show jumper was temporarily stripped of his victory in the British Show Jumping Derby for making a V sign?

6. Who earned the first perfect score in the history of Olympic gymnastics at the 1976 Summer Olympics in Montreal?

7. In 1979, who became the first tennis player to earn more than one million dollars in prize money in a single season?

SEVENTIES SPORT 2

8. In 1976, which Liverpool player became the captain of England?

9. How many gold medals did 22 year-old American swimmer Mark Spitz win in the 1972 Summer Olympics in Munich?

10. In 1974, which tennis player defeated Ken Rosewall in the finals of Wimbledon and the US Open?

11. 6 ft 11 in, 49 stone Martin Austin Ruane and 6ft 6 in, 26 stone Shirley Crabtree were the pre-eminent wrestling rivals during the seventies. By what names are they remembered?

12. Which tennis player won the first of his four US Open titles in 1979 at the age of twenty?

13. Name the British Judo champion who won the British Final and the first European Final of the BBC programme *Superstars* in 1979.

14. In 1978, who did Muhammad Ali beat to win the World Heavyweight Championship for the third time?

15. In 1972, Palestinian terrorists from which organisation invaded the Olympic Village and killed 11 Israeli athletes and coaches?

16. In 1971, which team won the English County Championship for the first time since 1913 in their centenary year?

17. In 1970, the Giro d'Italia and the Tour de France were won by which Belgian cycling legend?

18. Which Canadian-bred, Irish-trained three year-old Thoroughbred racehorse won all three English Triple Crown Races and the Irish Derby in 1970?

19. He was the first Latino baseball player to win a World Series as a starter (1960), and receive a National League MVP Award (1966), and he died in a plane crash on New Year's Eve 1972. What was his name?

20. Which British racing driver won the Formula One World Drivers' Championship in 1976 in his first year with McLaren?

Elizabeth II and the Silver
Jubilee

1. What was the official anniversary date?

2. True or false: The Queen and Prince Philip broke a record by visiting 28 counties in the UK during a three-month period in 1977?

3. What did they use during their tour of Scotland so that they didn't have to return to Holyroodhouse each evening?

4. On 6th June, a chain of bonfire beacons was lit across the country. The Queen lit the first one, where?

5. On 7th June, where did the Royal Family attend a Service of Thanksgiving?

6. In the afternoon, an estimated one million people crowded along which street to see The Queen?

7. On 7th June, she watched a procession of 400 what?

8. How many million people around the world watched the day's events live on television: 200 million, 500 million, 1.2 billion?

9. On which day were most of the street parties held around the country?

10. On which day did The Queen sail down the Thames from Greenwich to Lambeth?

11. The voyage was a re-enactment of which historical British monarch?

12. What was the trip's official name?

13. Which two commemorative landmarks did The Queen open during the trip?

14. That week the Sex Pistols' anti-monarchy song 'God Save the Queen' was kept off the top of the pop charts by which Rod Stewart single?

15. Which bridge in London was painted red, white and blue for the Silver Jubilee and has kept the colour scheme ever since?

16. On 28th June, The Queen reviewed the Fleet at Spithead from where?

17. Name the Australian artist who was commissioned to complete the only official portrait of The Queen during the Silver Jubilee year.

18. True or false: during 1977, The Queen travelled an estimated 56,000 miles?

19. Which town was granted city status in honour of the Silver Jubilee?

20. The Royal Mint issued a commemorative crown piece. What was its face value?

Seventies

Sitcoms

1. What was Terry and June's surname in *Happy Ever After*?

2. What was the name of the department store in *Are You Being Served*?

3. What was the occupation of frustrated 'stay at home' housewife Ria Parkinson's husband in *Butterflies*?

4. Which seventies sitcom was set in the fictional Yorkshire town of Scarsdale?

5. Which seventies sitcom was set in the fictional Fenn Street School?

6. Why was *Man About The House* considered daring at the time?

7. What was the first name of Bob's (Rodney Bewes) prissy librarian fiancée played by Brigit Forsyth in *Whatever Happened To The Likely Lads*?

8. What was Windsor Davies' ear-splitting catchphrase in *It Ain't Half Hot Mum*?

9. What was the name of the Inspector in *On The Buses*?

10. Which seventies sitcom was set in 'Paradise Lodge Retirement Home'?

11. The BBC1 sitcom *Sykes* ran from 1972. Why did it abruptly end in October 1980?

12. Who played the lodger Gavin Rumsey in *The Cuckoo Waltz*?

13. What was the name of Lynda Barron's character in *Open All Hours*?

14. In which seventies sitcom did Norman Eshley play a snobbish middle-class estate agent called Jeffrey Fourmile?

15. In *Citizen Smith*, Wolfie was the self-proclaimed leader of which revolutionary organisation?

16. What mental image occurred to Reginald Perrin every time he thought of his mother-in-law?

17. Which seventies sitcom was set in Walmington-on-Sea?

18. Who lived on Oil Drum Lane, a fictional street in Shepherd's Bush, London?

19. What was the name of Rigsby's pampered cat in *Rising Damp*?

20. What was the name of Betty and Frank's daughter in *Some Mothers Do 'Ave 'Em*?

★ Star Wars ★

1. During development what was Luke Skywalker originally called?

2. What did 20th Century Fox agree to give director George Lucas instead of a large salary – representing one of the biggest mistakes in film history?

3. In early drafts of the screenplay, which character was originally called Buffy?

4. Which role did Anthony Daniels play?

5. Which role did Kenny Baker play?

6. What spacecraft had to be redesigned at short notice because the original model too closely resembled one from the 1970s British TV series *Space: 1999*?

7. Which character came from the planet Kashyyyk?

8. True or false: before it was decided to use animatronics for Yoda, he was nearly played by a performing monkey?

9. Which of these actors was considered for the part of Han Solo: Tom Selleck, Kurt Russell, Christopher Walken, Sylvester Stallone, Al Pacino?

10. How many times was the word 'ewok' uttered in the *Star Wars* films?

11. R2D2 was named after what?

12. How much was Harrison Ford paid for his performance in the first film: $10,000, $100,000 or $1,000,000?

13. What was the home planet of C-3PO?

14. What inspired the shape of the Millennium Falcon?

15. Jawaese (spoken by Jawas) was based on a speeded-up version of which African language?

16. Who directed *The Empire Strikes Back*?

17. Which character was nearly dressed in a pair of baggy shorts because studio executives felt he was too naked?

18. Which *Star Wars* actor dismissed the films as 'fairy-tale rubbish'?

19. Which pioneering actor/director did George Lucas originally want for the voice of Darth Vader before deciding he was too recognisable?

20. Who earned millions for 4.5 hours work on *The Empire Strikes Back* after demanding a quarter of one per cent of the film's total gross?

Seventies Fads and

Crazes

1. Which iconic children's bicycle was branded as 'THE HoT oNE'?

2. Which plastic flying toy had its origins in circular pie tins in a bakery in Bridgeport Connecticut?

3. Fill in the blank: '_____ wobble, but they don't fall down.'

4. What nationality is the spoon-bending self-publicist, Uri Geller?

5. Who wrote the popular pseudoscientific extraterrestrial bestseller, *Chariots of The Gods*?

6. What was the name of the coloured plastic balls that children fitted to the spokes of their bikes during the seventies?

7. What string figure game popular during the seventies was known in America as Jack in the Pulpit?

8. During the seventies, what game did children play with a long loop of elastic and two chairs?

9. Originally called the 'Pon-Pon' by its Italian inventor, how is this large children's toy better known?

10. In July 1973, the green shield stamp catalogue business was rebranded under what new name?

11. In which ocean is the Bermuda Triangle located?

12. In 1975, a song about ending an adulterous relationship spent six weeks at the top of the UK pop charts. What was its name?

13. What was the name of the plastic toy that used thin cardboard disks containing seven small stereoscopic 3-D pairs of photographs?

14. Which short-lived seventies fad was conceived by a Californian advertising executive after joking that it would make the perfect pet as it wouldn't need feeding?

15. Name the best-selling pocket-sized analogue stylus-operated keyboard that ceased production in 1975.

16. Name the clear, colourless fruit brandy found in a Black Forest gateau.

17. The licence plates of which anthropomorphic car read OFP 857?

18. Name the nine-year-old who topped the UK pop chart for five weeks in 1972 with the hit single 'Long Haired Lover From Liverpool'.

19. Which popular seventies dish is also known as *côtelette de volaille*?

20. Name the American actor who was originally offered the role of Danny in *Grease* but turned it down because he didn't want to be typecast.

Meryl

★ Streep ★

1. In which year was she born?

2. In which US state was she born and raised?

3. At which Ivy League university did she study Drama?

4. Which other now famous actress was her classmate at university?

5. In 1976, what did she win for her performance in Tennessee Williams' play 27 *Wagons Full of Cotton*?

6. She began auditioning for film roles after being inspired by Robert De Niro's performance in which 1976 film?

7. In 1976, she auditioned unsuccessfully for the lead role in a Dino De Laurentis film that went to Jessica Lange. Name the film.

8. In which film starring Jane Fonda and Vanessa Redgrave did she make her film debut?

9. Who suggested Streep for her role in *The Deer Hunter* after seeing her in a Broadway production of *The Cherry Orchard*?

10. What was the name of her partner, who appeared in *The Deer Hunter* while suffering from lung cancer, and died the following year?

11. In 1978, she won the Primetime Emmy Award for Lead Actress for her performance in which mini-series?

12. Which actress was offered Streep's role in *Kramer vs. Kramer*, but had to turn it down because of scheduling conflicts with *Charlie's Angels*?

13. Name the French director who turned down an offer to direct *Kramer vs. Kramer*.

14. In 1979, she played a supporting role in which Woody Allen film?

15. Which film earned her first Academy Award nomination?

16. Which film earned her first Academy Award win?

17. Who was her male co-star in *The Seduction of Joe Tynan* (1979)?

18. Which star of Hollywood's Golden Age considered Meryl Streep the least watchable of all the modern actresses?

19. Which star of Hollywood's Golden Age wrote Meryl Streep a letter telling her that she was her successor as the preeminent American actress?

20. How many Academy Award nominations (including wins) has she received to date: 9, 12 or 19?

Fawlty

★ Towers ★

1. In which seaside town was it set?

2. How many episodes were made?

3. Who was Donald Sinclair?

4. Who co-wrote the show with John Cleese?

5. What is the name of the Irish cowboy builder in 'The Builders' episode?

6. Which actor played the man who wanted his sausages?

7. Who played the irritating wisecracking Roger in 'The Anniversary' episode?

8. Basil thrashed his car with a tree branch in 'Gourmet Night'. What colour was it?

9. What was the name of the new Greek chef who got drunk after being romantically spurned by Manuel?

10. In which war did Basil receive the shrapnel wound that he always exaggerated during times of crisis?

11. How many men did Basil claim to have killed during his National Service?

12. What was the name of Manuel's 'hamster'?

13. Which bumbling character was played by Ballard Berkeley?

14. What were the names of the two elderly spinsters?

15. Why did the name 'Wooburn Grange Country Club' appear in some of the exterior shots of the hotel?

16. Which episode has John Cleese described as his favourite?

17. Who played Mr Hutchinson the spoon salesman in 'The Hotel Inspectors'?

18. What was the name of the horse that won Basil £75?

19. What aristocratic alter ego did the confidence trickster use in 'A Touch of Class'?

20. In 'Gourmet Night', what was Duck Surprise?

21. How did John Cleese get revenge on Richard Ingrams, the television reviewer for *The Spectator*, for his scathing review of the first series?

Grease

1. In which year is the film set?

2. What is the name of the school in the film?

3. Who was the front runner to play Sandy but objected to the final scene on religious grounds?

4. What is Sandy's surname in the film?

5. Before the film, who played the role of Danny Zuko on Broadway?

6. Elvis Presley turned down which role?

7. How old was John Travolta when filming began?

8. How old was Olivia Newton-John?

9. Before filming, who was the bigger star of the two?

10. Danny's windbreaker at the beginning of the film was a nod to which 1950s film?

11. Complete Principal McGee's line: 'If you can't be an athlete, be an _____.'

12. Why did some of the cast members get sick from filming the drag race scene?

13. Complete Rizzo's line: 'She looks too pure to be _____.'

14. What did Danny and Kenickie do to hide their embarrassment immediately after hugging?

15. Complete the sentence: 'A hickie from Kenickie is like a _____.'

16. Which scene was Olivia Newton-John terrified of filming and had to be persuaded by John Travolta?

17. Which character said the line, 'The only man a girl can depend on is her daddy'?

18. What were the T-Birds called in the play?

19. Which Academy Award-winning Olivia Newton-John solo song was written and performed after filming wrapped?

20. Which critically panned romantic comedy film reunited Travolta and Newton-John in 1983?

Name the actress in both
Films

1. *The Last Picture Show (1971), Taxi Driver (1976)*

2. *Chinatown (1974), Network (1976)*

3. *McCabe & Mrs. Miller (1971), Don't Look Now (1973)*

4. *Day for Night (1973), The Deep (1977)*

5. *Toomorrow (1970), Grease (1978)*

6. *The Great Gatsby (1974), The Haunting of Julia (1977)*

7. *Myra Breckinridge (1970), Mother, Jugs & Speed (1976)*

8. *Klute (1971), The China Syndrome (1979)*

9. *A Star Is Born (1976), The Way We Were (1973)*

10. *There's a Girl in My Soup (1970), Foul Play (1978)*

11. *The Deer Hunter (1978), Kramer vs. Kramer (1979)*

12. *Le Sauvage (1975), Hustle (1975)*

13. *Carnal Knowledge (1971), The Wind and the Lion (1975)*

14. *The Last Picture Show (1971), Alice Doesn't Live Here Anymore (1974)*

15. *Won Ton Ton: The Dog Who Saved Hollywood (1976), Close Encounters of the Third Kind (1977)*

16. *Carrie (1976), 3 Women (1977)*

17. *Taxi Driver* (1976), *Bugsy Malone* (1976)

18. *Annie Hall* (1977), *3 Women* (1977)

19. *The Godfather* (1972), *Annie Hall* (1977)

20. *The Effect of Gamma Rays on Man-in-the-Moon Marigolds* (1972), *The Drowning Pool* (1975)

21. *The Big Bird Cage* (1972), *Foxy Brown* (1974)

22. *Annie Hall* (1977), *Alien* (1979)

23. *Live and Let Die* (1973), *Sinbad and the Eye of the Tiger* (1977)

24. *Women in Love* (1969), *A Touch of Class* (1973)

25. *Myra Breckinridge* (1970), *Logan's Run* (1976)

26. *Shampoo* (1975), *Star Wars* (1977)

27. *Love Story* (1970), *The Getaway* (1972)

28. *King Kong* (1976), *All That Jazz* (1979)

29. *Mary, Queen of Scots* (1971), *Agatha* (1979)

30. *Perfect Friday* (1970), *The Loves and Times of Scaramouche* (1976)

MORE

★ Science ★

1. Who predicted Hawking radiation in 1974?

2. On 4th April 1973, Martin Cooper, the head of Motorola's communications systems division, made the world's first handheld mobile phone call. True or false: the phone weighed nearly a kilogramme?

3. In the journal *Emergency Medicine* in 1974 an American thoracic surgeon revealed his new technique of abdominal thrusts to treat choking. What was his name?

4. On 24th November 1974, a group of paleoanthropologists discovered a 3.2-million-year-old skeleton of an *Australopithecus afarensis*. What did they name this important specimen?

5. On 18th May 1974, 'Smiling Buddha', India's first what took place underground at Pokhran?

6. On 26th June 1974, the sale of a packet of Wrigley's chewing gum at the Marsh Supermarket in Troy, Ohio was the first use of what technology?

7. What 3-D puzzle – devised by a Hungarian professor of architecture called Ernö in 1974 – went on to sell more than 350 million worldwide after it hit the shelves six years later?

8. In April 1975, India launched its first satellite, named after a 5th-century astronomer and mathematician from India. What was his name?

9. Which planetary probe did NASA launch on 20th August 1975?

10. The MITS Altair 8800 was launched in January 1975; it was the world's first what?

11. On 4th April 1975, Bill Gates and Paul Allen formed a company called 'Micro Soft' in Albuquerque, New Mexico to develop and sell BASIC software for which microcomputer?

12. Which infectious disease – commonly spread by ticks – was first identified at Lyme, Connecticut in 1975?

13. On 31st July 1976, NASA released a controversial photograph of the Cydonia Region on the surface of the planet Mars, taken by the probe Viking 1. What did it appear to show?

14. In 1976, evolutionary biologist Richard Dawkins published a book on the gene-centred view of evolution. What was its title?

15. In 1976, Electric Pencil was released, the first software of its kind for home computers. What did it do?

16. In 1977, biologists successfully did what for the first time with a tiny bacterium-infecting virus called Phi X 174?

17. On 11th September 1977, Atari Inc. released its first home video game console. What was it called?

18. In December 1977, a Lockheed jet codenamed *Have Blue* became the first aircraft of its kind to fly. What was it?

19. Which German-born American physicist and rocket engineer died on 16th June 1977?

20. The first spreadsheet programme was released in 1979, initially for the Apple II computer. What was its name?

Name the Novelist

Books

1. *Interview with a Vampire*

2. *The Shining*

3. *The Thorn Birds*

4. *Roots*

5. *The World According to Garp*

6. *Carrie*

7. *All Creatures Great and Small*

8. *The Exorcist*

9. *Sophie's Choice*

10. *Breakfast of Champions*

11. *Tinker, Tailor, Soldier, Spy*

12. *Zen and the Art of Motorcycle Maintenance*

NAME THE NOVELIST — BOOKS

13. **All the President's Men**

14. **84, Charing Cross Road**

15. **The Day of the Jackal**

16. **The Executioner's Song**

17. **Deliverance**

18. **Smiley's People**

19. **Love Story**

20. **Rabbit Redux**

21. **Watership Down**

22. **The Princess Bride**

23. **Shōgun**

24. **Fear of Flying**

25. **Gravity's Rainbow**

26. **Kane and Abel**

27. **The Sea, The Sea**

28. **The Right Stuff**

29. **The French Lieutenant's Woman**

30. **The Conservationist**

★ Advertising 2 ★

1. Which English actor, usually typecast as an upper class fop or a stammering vicar, sang the television jingle 'P . . . p . . . pick up a Penguin'?

2. Name the powdered packet juice drink sold by Kellogg's that came in five flavours: orange, grapefruit, pineapple, lemon and blackcurrant.

3. Which chocolate bar was advertised with a famous jingle that was based on the English folk song 'The Lincolnshire Poacher'?

4. Name the chewy round Nestlé toffees that were stacked end to end in a red tube.

5. Which brand of drink was advertised by an animated polar bear wearing sunglasses and the slogan, 'It's frothy, man'?

6. True or false: Space Dust – the powdery sweet that fizzed and popped on your tongue – was withdrawn from sale after a child choked to death?

7. How much did a packet of Spangles cost in 1974?

8. When he worked in advertising, which future Formula One motorsport commentator invented the slogan, 'Opal Fruits: made to make your mouth water'?

9. 'A drink's too wet without one.' Without what?

10. Which brand of drink used the slogan: 'Every bubble's passed its fizzical'?

11. Which breakfast cereal was 'For grown up people who'd rather not grow anymore'?

12. Which washing powder claimed to 'Get your whites right'?

13. Which brand of lager 'Puts out the fire'?

14. What product did Fernville Lord Digby advertise during the seventies?

15. Who voiced the advert with the slogan 'Everyone's a fruit and nutcase'?

16. What was 'Lipsmackin' thirstquenchin' acetastin' motivatin' goodbuzzin' cooltalkin' highwalkin' fastlivin' evergivin' coolfizzin'?

17. The advertisement for which beauty product asked, 'Is she or isn't she?'

18. Name the light curly potato snack that was, 'positively scruncherous'?

19. Which toy company used the slogan, 'just add children'?

20. Which company 'had the knack of producing the right car at the right time?'

Rocky

1. In which year was the film released?

2. How many days did it take Stallone to write the first draft of the script?

3. True or false: in Stallone's original script, Rocky threw the final fight?

4. Which professional heavyweight boxer was lined up to play Apollo Creed but dropped out at the last minute?

5. Who insulted Stallone's acting and fighting while sparring in his audition, without realising that he was the star and author?

6. How long did filming take: 28, 42 or 96 days?

7. Which future Academy Award winner auditioned for the role of Adrian but was judged to be too attractive?

8. Who played the role of Adrian?

9. Where did Adrian work?

10. What was the name of Rocky's trainer, played by Burgess Meredith?

11. What was Rocky's dog called?

12. At the end of the training montage, Rocky ran to the top of the steps of which building?

13. What was John G. Avildsen's contribution to the film?

14. Rocky worked out by punching sides of beef at which meat packing plant?

15. True or false: Rocky never said the iconic phrase 'Yo, Adrian' during the film?

16. True or false: the actual gloves used in the final fight were illegal in the US, but they were used because they looked right?

17. The actress who played Adrian was the younger sister of which famous film director?

18. True or false: Rocky lived at 1616 West Tusculum Street, Philadelphia PA 19134?

19. Only one other actor has the distinction of being nominated for an Academy Award as sole writer of an original screenplay and for the leading role in the same film. Who?

20. True or false: executives at United Artists cast Stallone by mistake by focusing on the wrong actor while watching a clip from Stallone's earlier film, *The Lords of Flatbush*?

Seventies

Blockbusters

1. *Love Story* (1970) was one of the highest grossing films in the US of all time. What was the name of its 1978 sequel?

2. Charles Gray, who played Henderson in *You Only Live Twice* (1967), returned as which character in *Diamonds Are Forever* (1971)?

3. Which 1972 American crime drama film began with the words, 'I believe in America'?

4. Who directed the coming of age comedy-drama blockbuster *American Graffiti* (1973)?

5. Who was the studio's first choice for Max von Sydow's role in *The Exorcist* (1973) until the director vetoed this decision?

6. Many characters are seen drinking which brand of beer during *The Sting* (1973)?

7. Which 1974 Mel Brooks cowboy blockbuster was originally called *Tex X*?

8. The highest grossing film released in 1974 starred Paul Newman and Steve McQueen and the cast included Fred Astaire, Richard Chamberlain, Faye Dunaway, O. J. Simpson and Robert Wagner. What was its title?

9. Which Hollywood star played Randle Patrick McMurphy (Jack Nicholson) on stage and tried to get the film *One Flew Over the Cuckoo's Nest* (1975) made during the sixties?

10. Which member of The Rolling Stones asked to play Frank-N-Furter in *The Rocky Horror Picture Show* (1975)?

11. What was the name of Quint's fishing boat in *Jaws* (1975)?

12. Stallone was inspired to write *Rocky* (1976) after watching which journeyman survive fifteen rounds with Muhammad Ali and even knock him down?

13. What was the name of the disco in *Saturday Night Fever* (1977)?

14. While filming *Star Wars* (1977), what secret did Mark Hamill manage to keep even from co-star Harrison Ford and his own wife?

15. Who turned down the role of Roy Neary (Richard Dreyfuss) on *Close Encounters of the Third Kind* (1977) because he claimed he was unable to cry on cue?

16. What nickname did Bo 'Bandit' Darville (Burt Reynolds) give Carrie (Sally Field) in *Smokey and the Bandit* (1977)?

17. What was the name of John Belushi's character in *Animal House* (1978)?

18. How many times is the word 'grease' used in the film *Grease* (1978)?

19. Olympic champion decathlete Caitlyn Jenner (formerly known as Bruce Jenner) auditioned for the title role in which 1978 Richard Donner film?

20. What was the character name of the little boy in *Kramer vs. Kramer* (1979)?

More Children's
Television

1. Which cartoon featured a funny green dog, a pink cat and very wobbly animation?

2. Name the programme – the first of its kind on British television – that aired live for its first episode on 4th April 1972, with a report on ospreys in Scotland.

3. Fifty cartoon adventures were made starring Crystal Tipps and her dog Alistair. What colour was Crystal's hair?

4. What was the name of the 'invisible' race of Martians in the marionette-based sixties science-fiction TV series *Captain Scarlet* that was repeated during the seventies?

5. Which BBC newsreader narrated the animated children's television series *Mary, Mungo and Midge*?

6. Which programme broadcast on Tuesdays and Fridays was a deliberate Thames TV rival to the BBC's *Blue Peter*, which aired on Mondays and Thursdays?

7. Which character predated *Sesame Street* by three years and was first designed for a cracker commercial: Cookie Monster, Big Bird or Grover?

8. Which cartoon sporting team travelled in a van with their elderly coach, Granny and a team dog mascot called Dribbles?

9. The first episode of *Record Breakers* aired on 15th December 1972. How many records did its presenter, Roy Castle, himself break on the show: 3, 9 or 18?

10. Name the futuristic series starring Martin Landau and Barbara Bain that was the most expensive produced for British television when it first aired on 4th September 1975.

11. Which cartoon starred a titular 'mild-mannered janitor'?

12. Name the educational children's programme presented by the pipe-smoking Jack Hargreaves and Fred Dinenage that featured lots of facts, tricks and games.

13. Whose souvenirs included a wooden spoon, a parrot's feather and a photo of a herd of elephants?

14. What was the name of the science-fiction television series that first ran from 1973 to 1979 on ITV about a special team of telepathic children with the ability to teleport using bracelets?

15. Why were there two teddies on *Play School*?

16. What is the English title of the Yugoslavian children's programme *Počitnice v Lipici* which was repeated during the seventies and featured a young teenage girl, Julia, on a stud farm run by her Uncle Dimitri?

17. Which programme aired on BBC2 on Saturday afternoons from 1971–1984 with presenters that included Toni Arthur, Chloe Ashcroft, Johnny Ball, Floella Benjamin, Brian Cant, Derek Griffiths, Jeremy Irons and Tony Robinson?

18. Which comedy show, first broadcast by the BBC on 6th January 1976, featured red motley suited jester Timothy Claypole (Michael Staniforth)?

19. On the opening credits of which show would you have heard the words: 'Flight com, I can't hold her! She's breaking up! She's breaking—'?

20. What was the name of the policeman on the animated cartoon *Top Cat* (later renamed *Boss Cat*)?

★ Jaws ★

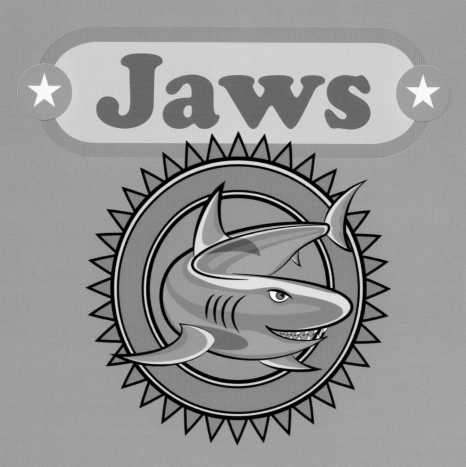

1. Who wrote the book *Jaws*?

2. Which of these was a suggested title for the book: *A Silence in the Deep, The Stillness in the Water, Leviathan Rising, Jaws of Death* or *Jaws of Leviathan*?

3. Producers Richard Zanuck and David Brown hired Spielberg because they felt the film was thematically similar to which of his earlier films?

4. What role did stuntwoman Susan Backlinie play?

5. How many mechanical sharks were made for the film, at a cost of $250,000 each?

6. The production budget nearly trebled from its initial $3.5 million but its box office total is currently: $256 million, $471 million or $742 million?

7. At which resort in Massachusetts were the beach scenes filmed?

8. Which friend of Spielberg rejected the role of Brody, fearing it would make him too famous?

9. Jon Voight, Timothy Bottoms and Jeff Bridges all turned down which role?

10. Who was Spielberg's first choice to play Quint?

11. Who did Spielberg cast after meeting him at a party?

12. Who described Robert Shaw (Quint) as 'the most extraordinarily, unnecessarily competitive person he'd ever met'?

13. Who received an Academy Award for writing the famous musical score?

14. When Spielberg first heard the *Jaws* theme played on a piano, how did he react?

15. During Quint's 'Indianapolis Speech' on the boat, he mentioned how to estimate the length of a shark: 'You tell by looking from the _____ to the _____.'

16. Spielberg nicknamed the shark Bruce after his: lawyer, dentist or psychiatrist?

17. What role did Murray Hamilton play?

18. During the story, a large tourist billboard was defaced by a shark's tail and a speech bubble. What did it say?

19. Steven Spielberg shot roughly a quarter of the film from what perspective?

20. Which actor allegedly refused to work for Spielberg after being turned down for the role of Brody?

Here today, gone

Tomorrow

1. Nottingham-based pop group Paper Lace had brief success in 1974 with which war-themed song?

2. In which year did The Manhattan Transfer reach the top of the UK Singles Chart with 'Chanson D'Amour'?

3. In 1970, which British rock group sang 'Have a drink, have a drive, go out and see what you can find'?

4. Clive Dunn reached No. 1 in 1971 with which song?

5. Name the British glam rock band that had a hit in 1973 with 'See My Baby Jive'.

6. Gilbert O'Sullivan spent two weeks at No. 1 in the UK Singles Chart in 1972 with a love song of an uncle for his young niece. What was her name?

7. In 1973, The Hot Shots reached No. 4 in the UK Singles Chart with a novelty song featuring Charlie Brown's pet beagle from the comic strip *Peanuts*. What was its title?

8. What was the title of the 1975 UK No. 1 single by Windsor Davies and Don Estelle?

9. The Scottish rock band Pilot topped the UK Singles Chart in February 1975 singing about which month of the year?

10. What was unusual about the vocal stylings of Telly Savalas in his 1975 one-hit-wonder, 'If'?

HERE TODAY, GONE TOMORROW

11. Who had a UK hit in 1975 with 'Funky Moped'?

12. What nationality was the band Pussycat who had a worldwide hit in 1975 with 'Mississippi'?

13. Who sold 60 million albums and became a bearded, kaftan-wearing sex symbol during the seventies?

14. In which C.W. McCall hit did Rubber Duck complain about the smell of hogs?

15. What was the name of the motorcycle gang leader who died in The Shangri-Las' hit song, 'Leader Of The Pack'?

16. In which year did Brian & Michael's song 'Matchstalk Men And Matchstalk Cats And Dogs' reach No. 1 in the UK?

17. Name the 1978 hit by Boney M. that is one of the top ten all-time best-selling singles in the UK.

18. Brotherhood Of Man had three No. 1 hits in the UK during the seventies. Name two of them.

19. David Soul spent four weeks at No. 1 in the UK Singles Chart in early 1977 with which song?

20. In 1978, Irish flautist James Galway reached No. 3 in the UK singles chart with his instrumental version of which John Denver hit?

Al

★ Pacino ★

1. In which year was he born?

2. What is Al short for?

3. When he was a teenager, what did his friends call him?

4. What was his childhood sporting ambition?

5. He trained at The Actors Studio in New York City, under which famous acting teacher?

6. His first starring feature film role was in the 1971 film *The Panic in Needle Park*. What was its main theme?

7. Which hard-living American singer-songwriter, who died ten days before the film's release, was initially considered for Pacino's role?

8. In 1973, he played Lion, a homeless ex-sailor in *Scarecrow*. Who played the character Max?

9. In which film did he play first-time crook Sonny Wortzik, attempting to rob the First Brooklyn Savings Bank?

10. What part did he play in *The Godfather* and *The Godfather Part II*?

11. Between 1973 and 1976, he was nominated for an Academy Award for *The Godfather* and *The Godfather Part II* and which two other films?

12. Who did he briefly date while they were filming *The Godfather*?

13. Why did he boycott the 1973 Academy Award Ceremony?

14. In 1976, he was director John Schlesinger's first choice, but producers cast Dustin Hoffman instead. Name the film.

15. In 1977, he won his second what for his performance in *The Basic Training of Pavlo Hummel*?

16. Name the 1977 film in which he played an American racing driver.

17. He turned down the lead role in which Stephen Spielberg film?

18. Which seventies film did he shoot in reverse order, beginning with long hair and beard and ending clean-cut?

19. What was the name of the 1979 courtroom drama that earned him his fifth Academy Award nomination?

20. He turned down Martin Sheen's role in which 1979 film?

I L♥VE THAILAND

Top of the

Pops

1. Who had a hit in 1974 with 'Kung Fu Fighting'?

2. In which year did Queen release 'Bohemian Rhapsody'?

3. In 1970, which American group made music history by reaching the top of the charts with their first four singles: 'I Want You Back', 'ABC', 'The Love You Save' and 'I'll Be There'?

4. In 1979, which song gave Cliff Richard his first No. 1 hit since 'Congratulations' eleven years earlier?

5. Which Tony Orlando & Dawn song was the best-selling single of 1973?

6. Which solo song, released on 11th October 1971, did *Rolling Stone* describe as John Lennon's 'greatest musical gift to the world'.

7. In which year did Status Quo release its tenth studio album, *Rockin' All Over the World*?

8. On 10th August 1979, Michael Jackson broke away from Motown Records with the release of which solo album?

9. Which English band released the single 'Sex & Drugs & Rock & Roll' on 26th August 1977?

10. How old was Kate Bush when she wrote her debut hit single 'Wuthering Heights'?

11. The cover to which iconic 1979 album features a photo of bassist Paul Simonon smashing his Fender Precision Bass?

12. Blondie's 'Heart of Glass' was the second-highest selling single of 1979 in the UK; which song by Art Garfunkel was the highest?

13. Who had a hit with 'You Make Me Feel Like Dancing'?

14. Who sang the hits 'I Love to Love (But My Baby Loves to Dance)' and 'Dance Little Lady Dance'?

15. Terry Jacks had one of the biggest-selling singles of all time by a Canadian, with which 1974 song?

16. The opening riff of which 1977 ABBA No. 1 hit was inspired by Stevie Wonder's 'I Wish'?

17. Which English glam rock band had a hit in 1974 with 'Tiger Feet'?

18. What was Alvin Stardust's only UK No. 1?

19. Which group released the 1973 hit 'You Won't Find Another Fool Like Me'?

20. In 1977, 'Nobody Does It Better' by Carly Simon was the theme tune for which James Bond film?

Famous TV

Catchphrases

Which TV programmes are associated with these phrases?

1. 'Shazbot!'

2. 'Good night, John Boy'

3. 'De plane! De plane!'

4. 'Don't make me angry. You wouldn't like me when I'm angry.'

5. 'You're all doing very well!'

6. 'Don't just stand there, do something.'

7. 'Hello Honky Tonks.'

8. 'Wocka, wocka.'

9. 'Zoinks!'

10. 'Good morning angels.'

11. 'And in a packed programme tonight . . .'

12. 'Ooh . . . Betty!'

13. 'No one expects the Spanish Inquisition.'

14. 'I'm free!'

15. 'Permission to speak, Sir!'

16. 'You dirty old man.'

17. 'Thank you very much, Jerry!'

18. 'Power to the People!'

19. 'Ooh, you are awful but I like you!'

20. 'All right, Mr la-di-da Gunner Graham . . .'

21. 'I didn't get where I am today without . . .'

22. 'Didn't he/she do well?'

23. 'I'll have a half.'

24. 'I've started so I'll finish.'

25. 'Has he been?'

26. 'And now for something completely different.'

27. 'You can't see the join!'

28. 'Ha-ha, ha-ha, ha-ha, boom boom!'

29. 'Get your trousers on – you're nicked.'

30. 'You rang?'

Opening Lines – Name That

Tune

1. 'At first I was afraid I was petrified.'

2. 'Wake up Maggie I think I got something to say to you.'

3. 'I'm . . . I'm so in love with you.'

4. 'Mister, your eyes are full of hesitation, sure makes me wonder if you know what you're looking for.'

5. 'You can dance, you can jive, having the time of your life.'

6. 'I remember all my life, raining down as cold as ice.'

7. 'Well you're dirty and sweet, clad in black, don't look back and I love you.'

8. 'Finished with my woman 'cause she couldn't help me with my mind.'

9. 'I don't want to lose you, this good thing that I got 'cause if I do . . .'

10. 'Strumming my pain with his fingers, singing my life with his words.'

11. 'Holly came from Miami F.L.A.'

12. 'L.A. Proved too much for the man.'

13. 'We all came out to Montreux on the Lake Geneva shoreline.'

14. 'Mother, mother, there's too many of you crying.'

15. 'Well, you can tell by the way I use my walk, I'm a woman's man: no time to talk.'

16. 'We were rippin' up, we were rockin' up, roll it over and lay it down.'

17. 'We were at a party. His ear lobe fell in the deep.'

18. 'Young man, there's no need to feel down.'

19. 'Sup up your beer and collect your fags, there's a row going on down near Slough.'

20. 'Ooh, my little pretty one, my pretty one. When you gonna give me some time—'

CLOSE ENCOUNTERS OF THE

★ Third Kind ★

1. When did Spielberg begin developing the film?

2. In which year was the film finally released?

3. The discovery of a missing squadron of German planes was made in which desert?

4. What was Roy Neary's (Richard Dreyfuss) job?

5. Who played his wife, Ronnie?

6. What was located at 1613 Carlisle Drive East in Mobile, Indiana?

7. True or false: Marlon Brando turned down the lead role because he felt that he would be overshadowed by the special effects?

8. Which film director played the role of French scientist, Claude Lacombe?

9. What was the first line spoken in the film?

10. Who wrote the musical score?

11. Who was cast a few days before filming and was nominated for an Academy Award for her performance?

12. In which state was the secret landing zone for the UFOs built?

13. Spielberg conducted a few tests of which fledgling technology and decided against its use in this film?

14. What did Roy Neary do at the end of the film?

15. Without which legendary visual effects supervisor has Spielberg said, 'I'd still be on the Columbia back lot trying to get a cloud to materialize from thin air'?

16. What can be seen hanging upside down on the mothership as it flies over Devils Tower?

17. CE3K opened the same week that which other film overtook Spielberg's *Jaws* to become the biggest blockbuster in history?

18. During production, Spielberg repeatedly watched which 1956 seminal John Ford western?

19. Spielberg earned millions by making a wager with a director friend – they agreed that they would each give the other 2.5 per cent of the profits of their respective films. Who was his friend and what was the film?

20. How many Academy Award nominations did it receive?

Even More Children's

Television

1. Which numbered Thunderbirds were the orange space rocket and the yellow mini submarine?

2. What was the name of the French black-and-white television series set in the French Alps that featured a six-year-old boy and his Pyrenean Mountain Dog?

3. Who played the character Aunt Sally in *Worzel Gummidge* on ITV?

4. In the opening credits of *The Pink Panther Show* what did the Pink Panther hold in his hand?

5. In *The Bionic Woman* (1976–8), how did tennis pro Jaime Sommers (played by Lindsay Wagner) sustain the life-threatening injuries that led to her bionic implant surgery?

6. What was 'The Mystery Machine'?

7. Which surreal comedy show that ran from November 1970 to February 1980 on BBC2 and starred three Cambridge University graduates was titled 'The Super Chaps Three' during development?

8. Which animated American television series was set in the Stone Age town of Bedrock?

9. Which paper puppet programme featured a grey mouse, a tortoise called Flash, a seagull called Gulliver and a red shrimp called Scampi?

10. What was the name of the female ring-tailed lemur who appeared as a regular guest on the nature series, *Animal Magic*?

11. Which programme, broadcast between 28th March 1976 and 21st December 1980, was hosted by John Noakes and had an instrumental version of 'On Ilkla Moor Baht 'at' as its opening theme?

12. Which cartoon featured Muskie Muskrat, Moley Mole, Possible Possum, Ty Coon, Vincent Van Gopher, Inchworm, Pig Newton and its eponymous canine Sheriff?

13. How did Diana Prince (Lynda Carter) transform into Wonder Woman?

14. What was ECB1?

15. Which member of the teenage gang in *Scooby-Doo, Where Are You!* always wore an orange neckerchief and blue jeans?

16. *Grange Hill* was first shown on 8th February in which year?

17. Which show, that ran for two seasons between October 1973 and March 1975, was presented by Maggie and Fred and featured several puppets and wooden spoon characters?

18. Which 17-part show that ran from 1970 to 1971 included Melvyn Hayes as Albert, seven child characters: Billie, Brains, Doughnut, Scooper, Spring, Sticks, Tiger and an old red London Bus?

19. In the old Hanna-Barbera cartoon that repeated during the seventies, what were Pixie and Dixie and Mr Jinks?

20. Name the Hanna-Barbera animated sitcom that was aimed at adults but watched by children and featured the American suburban Boyle family.

Barbra

★ Streisand ★

1. In which year was she born?

2. What was her birth name?

3. In which part of New York did she grow up in near poverty following the death of her father?

4. What was her main objective: acting or singing?

5. Name the chess champion who was her contemporary at school and the object of her crush when she was sixteen years old.

6. Name the 1970 romantic comedy film in which she co-starred with George Segal.

7. She has been married twice. Both of her husbands starred in which 1970s conspiracy sci-fi thriller?

8. She divorced her first husband in 1971. What was his name?

9. She could have been the First Lady of which country?

10. Name the 1972 comedy film, directed by Peter Bogdanovich, in which she co-starred with Ryan O'Neal.

11. Barbra won her second Academy Award for her song 'Evergreen' from which 1976 film?

12. Being a Democratic Party supporter, she was on the official political enemy list of which disgraced American President?

13. Who was her co-star in the 1973 romantic drama film *The Way We Were?*

14. Name the 1979 duet with Barbra Streisand and Donna Summer.

15. Who was her co-star in *A Star is Born?*

16. Which singer did Barbra Streisand and her co-producer approach for the role, but his management insisted on top billing and demanded too much money?

17. Name the song by Neil Diamond and Barbra Streisand that topped the charts in 1978.

18. How many Grammy Award nominations has Streisand received: 21, 28 or 42?

19. Name the late film director who is currently the only other person apart from Streisand to have won an Emmy, Grammy, Oscar, Tony Award and a Peabody.

20. Because she has won numerous awards and is one of the best-selling female artists of all time she is often called what?

Iconic Film Quotations – Name the

Film

1. 'Food fight!'

2. 'I know what you're thinkin'. "Did he fire six shots or only five?"'

3. 'I guess you've noticed something a little strange with Dad. It's okay, though. I'm still Dad.'

4. 'Is it safe?'

5. 'James, how the hell do we get those diamonds down again?'

6. 'You can't just walk out of a drive-in.'

7. 'Follow the money . . . Just follow the money.'

8. 'Adrian!'

9. **'You talkin' to me?'**

10. **'You're gonna need a bigger boat.'**

11. **'But I tried, didn't I? Goddamnit, at least I did that.'**

12. ***'Glucklich zu sehen. Je suis enchante.'***

13. **'Go get the butter.'**

14. **'You – you've got me? Who's got you?'**

15. **'We gotta play with more bullets.'**

16. **'The Power of Christ compels you.'**

17. **'Your mother was a hamster and your father smelt of elderberries.'**

18. **'Leave the gun. Take the cannoli.'**

19. **'Terminate with extreme prejudice.'**

20. **'It's astounding . . . Time is . . . fleeting. Madness . . . takes its toll. But listen closely . . .'**

SEVENTIES CHILDREN'S

★ Books ★

Name the Novels in Which the Following Characters Appear:

1. Brothers, Fiver and Hazel

2. Buttercup, her true love, Westley, and Prince Humperdinck

3. A boy and the Once-ler

4. Jesse Aarons and Leslie Burke, his friend who lives next door

5. Bastian Balthazar Bux and the Childlike Empress of Fantastica

6. Mrs Frisby, a field mouse, Jeremy the Crow and a farmer named Fitzgibbon

7. Boggis, Bunce and Bean

8. Charlie, President Lancelot R. Gilligrass and the Vermicious Knids

9. Simon, Jane and Barney Drew and the Old Ones

10. Margaret, Nancy, Gretchen, Janie and a boy named Moose Freed

11. The citizens of a town named Chewandswallow

12. Danny, his father William and a cast of pheasants on sleeping tablets

SEVENTIES CHILDREN'S BOOKS

13. Carrie and Nick Willow, Albert Sandwich and Johnny Gotobed

14. Aunt Lucy and the Brown family of Windsor Gardens, London

15. Anna, Max and her Mama and Papa

16. Orphan Christina Parsons, her tyrannical Uncle William Russell and her cousins, Mark and Will

17. A little boy called Dave and his favourite stuffed toy dog

18. Jerry Renault and his friend Goober

19. Edmund Hooper and his father, Joseph

20. An unsuccessful witch named Meg and her stripy cat

Game and Quiz

Shows

1. Name the BBC1 quiz show featuring two teams consisting of four members of a single family.

2. Which Liverpudlian comedian was the host of *Winner Takes All*?

3. On *University Challenge* in 1975, how did the team from Victoria University of Manchester protest against Oxford and Cambridge colleges being able to enter separate teams?

4. Which game show had the famous opening 'And now from Norwich, it's the quiz of the week . . .'?

5. Frank Muir was one regular team captain of *Call My Bluff* during the seventies; which stammering Irish journalist was the other?

6. Metal Mickey made his screen debut on which British game show for children?

7. Who has been the host of the Radio 4 celebrity panel game *Quote . . . Unquote* since its first episode on 4th January 1976?

8. Which Liverpudlian comedian hosted *Name That Tune* from 1976 until 1983?

9. Which game show was co-hosted by Bob Monkhouse, Anne Aston and Wei Wei Wong?

GAME AND QUIZ SHOWS

10. Which game show featured the rounds: Personality, Mental Agility, Response, Observation, Physical Ability, Intelligence, General Knowledge and Super Round?

11. Which game show was hosted by Edward Woodward and then Jon Pertwee?

12. Which quiz show began with the ominous theme tune 'Approaching Menace' by the British composer Neil Richardson?

13. What was the name of Dusty Bin's Yorkshire Terrier on 3-2-1?

14. On which game show were the contestants introduced with the catchphrase: 'Let's meet the eight who are going to generate'?

15. Name the children's quiz show that was hosted by Michael Rodd.

16. In which show did one half of a couple wear a pair of headphones in a soundproof booth?

17. On which long-running quiz show was former England football captain Emlyn Hughes a team captain?

18. Who was the original host of *Give Us a Clue* when it launched in 1979?

19. What was the name of the BBC classical music quiz hosted by Joseph Cooper?

20. Who presented *Crackerjack* before Ed Stewart?

The Good

Life

1. What job did Tom quit in favour of self-sufficiency?

2. Which song did Tom frequently whistle *uptempo*?

3. What experiment did the Goods perform with three runner beans?

4. How did Tom power his generator?

5. Who always called Tom and Barbara 'Tim and Fatima'?

6. Margo briefly left Jerry after he refused to pay for a curio, in an attempt to curb her extravagant spending. What was it?

7. What was the name of Tom and Barbara's cockerel?

8. Tom stayed up all night on guard with an air rifle after the theft of eight what from his front garden?

9. What was their homemade wine made out of?

10. When Margo pretended to go horse riding, what was she actually doing?

11. What was the name of Margo's nemesis in the amateur dramatic society?

12. What part did Margo play in her amateur production of *The Sound of Music*?

13. What did the Goods use to dye Tom's home-woven suit green?

14. Name Tom and Barbara's two pigs.

15. Who was Geraldine?

16. What did Tom unsuccessfully try to sell to the owner of a restaurant called The Runcible Spoon?

17. Barbara and Margo enrolled in an evening class to learn which craft?

18. What did the Goods ask Margo to move because it was shadowing their crops?

19. Why did the Goods change their sleeping patterns, getting up and going to bed very early?

20. What was Douglas?

Farrah

★ Fawcett ★

1. In which year was she born?

2. What was her birth name?

3. In which US state did she grow up?

4. At High School, what title did she win four years in a row?

5. What did she study at university before dropping out to become a model?

6. In 1970, she appeared as 'Pretty Girl' in an episode of which sitcom starring David Cassidy?

7. Who did she marry in 1973?

8. When did she divorce?

9. What was the full name of her character in *Charlie's Angels*?

10. Name her two female co-stars on *Charlie's Angels*.

11. Which part was played by David Doyle?

12. What was the name of the detective agency?

13. She was paid $10,000 an episode for *Charlie's Angels*, but was earning far more from sales of what?

14. In 1978, she was offered the role in the film *Foul Play* that was subsequently played by which actress?

15. She appeared four times as three different characters; Kelly Wood, Trish Hollander and Victoria Webster in which American television series about a former astronaut?

16. With whom did she begin an 18-year relationship in 1979?

17. Why did that relationship end?

18. After her death from cancer in June 2009, who immediately removed a $20 million Andy Warhol portrait of her from her house, claiming ownership.

19. A court subsequently ruled in whose favour?

20. How many times during her career was she nominated for a Golden Globe Award: 1, 2 or 6?

Seventies

Sport 3

1. Who defeated Joe Frazier to win the World Heavyweight Boxing Championship on 22nd January 1973?

2. Which team won the Football League First Division title for the first time in its history on 9th May 1972?

3. On 20th April 1974, 25 year-old Australian Michael O'Brien became the first what at a major sporting event, during an England v France Rugby Union match at Twickenham?

4. On 30th October 1974 in Kinshasa, Zaire, Muhammad Ali's left hook knocked out which undefeated world heavyweight champion in the eighth round of 'The Rumble in the Jungle'?

5. On 5th May 1973, which team beat Leeds United 1–0 in the FA Cup Final at Wembley, becoming the first post-war winners outside the First Division?

6. Which former heavyweight boxing champion died on 30th December 1970 aged 38?

7. After suffering multiple fractures in a career threatening crash at the Daytona 200, who won the 500cc World Motorcycle Championship in 1976 and again the following year?

8. Virginia Wade won Wimbledon in 1977. What was her prize money: £13,500, £135,000 or £1.35 million?

9. Which Merseyside team won the Football League First Division title on 1st April 1970?

10. Which seventies American motorcycle daredevil earned a place in the *Guinness Book of World Records* after suffering more than 433 bone fractures during his career?

11. On 8th April 1974, which Braves outfielder hit his 715th career home run, surpassing Babe Ruth's long-standing record?

12. Nicknamed the 'Flying Scot', who won his second Formula 1 World Drivers' Championship driving a Tyrrell 001-Cosworth in 1971?

13. What year was the first FIFA World Cup to be televised in colour?

14. In 1973, who became the first player in NFL history to rush for more than 2,000 yards in a single season?

15. In 1974, who set a goal-scoring career record of 14 World Cup goals that stood for 32 years until it was broken by Brazil's Ronaldo?

16. Which Dutch football club won its third consecutive European Cup in 1973?

17. Name the Stoke City and England goalkeeper who announced his retirement from football in 1973 having lost the sight in one eye in a car crash.

18. On 12th August 1979, who knocked out Pete Ranzany in four rounds to win the NABF Welterweight Championship, his first professional title?

19. Which former Liverpool FC player released his debut single, 'Head Over Heels in Love' on 9th June 1979?

20. In Rugby Union, which team won the Grand Slam in 1976?

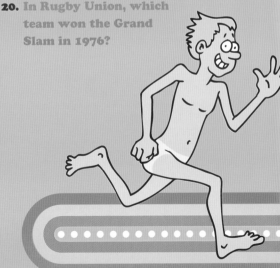

Answers

The Year That Was – 1970

1. It was reduced from 21 to 18
2. Half crown
3. Boeing 747
4. Mick Jagger
5. Hillman Avenger
6. Black Sabbath
7. Prince Charles
8. Rabies
9. Paul McCartney
10. Morris Marina
11. Rolls Royce
12. Fire
13. Bobby Moore
14. Laurence Olivier
15. Range Rover
16. Conservative Party
17. Edinburgh
18. Grog
19. Glastonbury Festival
20. Page Three girl

The Year That Was – 1971

1. Divorce
2. Open University
3. Aswan Dam
4. Postal workers
5. Rolls Royce
6. Radio licences were abolished
7. Evel Knievel
8. For destroying English language road signs in Wales
9. Gold
10. Biba
11. The Daily Mail
12. The Daily Sketch
13. Blue Peter
14. Reading Festival
15. Geoffrey Jackson
16. Free school milk
17. Satellite into orbit
18. Spaghetti Junction
19. The Queen
20. Health warnings

The Year That Was – 1972

1. Kurt Waldheim
2. RMS Queen Elizabeth
3. Derry/Londonderry
4. British Embassy
5. Miners
6. Trolleybus
7. Sri Lanka
8. William Whitelaw
9. Property
10. The Duke of Windsor (formerly Edward VIII)
11. Watergate
12. Gay Pride
13. Idi Amin (Uganda)
14. Bobby Fischer
15. Caerphilly
16. John Betjeman
17. Access
18. Walk on the moon
19. The Joy of Cooking
20. Unemployment

The Year That Was – 1973

1. The European Economic Community
2. Elvis Presley
3. London Bridge
4. London Stock Exchange
5. The Godfather
6. Value-added tax (VAT)
7. Pablo Picasso
8. The Sears Tower
9. The Ascent of Man
10. Skylab
11. The British Library
12. Its own postage stamps
13. Bobby Riggs
14. Yankee Stadium
15. Yom Kippur War/Arab–Israeli War
16. London Broadcasting Company (LBC)
17. The Dalai Lama
18. Princess Anne and Captain Mark Phillips
19. Carlos the Jackal
20. Pizza Hut

Answers

The Year That Was – 1974

1. Public holiday
2. The Three-Day Week
3. He lost the General Election he had called and Harold Wilson became Prime Minister.
4. He improved their pay offer.
5. Four
6. Lada
7. Carrie
8. ABBA
9. Manchester United
10. Planet of the Spiders
11. An IRA bomb exploded.
12. Don Revie
13. Brian Clough
14. Ceefax
15. Three
16. Woolwich
17. Lord Lucan
18. To preserve fuel
19. Edward Heath
20. Ching-Ching and Chia-Chia

The Year That Was – 1975

1. Space Mountain (Magic Kingdom)
2. Education Secretary
3. 35 per cent
4. Moorgate
5. Charlie Chaplin
6. Doctor Who
7. Monty Python and the Holy Grail
8. Vauxhall Chevette
9. The European Space Agency
10. Headingley
11. Gerald Ford
12. Fawlty Towers
13. Summit Mount Everest
14. York
15. 'Bohemian Rhapsody'
16. The Sex Pistols
17. Graham Hill
18. The Black Panther
19. Amity Island
20. Rabbi

The Year That Was – 1976

1. Concorde
2. Harold Wilson
3. Princess Margaret
4. Patty Hearst
5. Body Shop store
6. Apple
7. 'Save Your Kisses For Me'
8. James Callaghan
9. The CN Tower
10. Fiesta
11. Mars
12. Ladybird
13. Great Clock of Westminster (often referred to as a Big Ben)
14. Ebola
15. The Muppet Show
16. InterCity 125
17. The National Theatre (now called The Royal National Theatre)
18. The Sex Pistols
19. Bob Marley
20. Hotel California

The Year That Was – 1977

1. Uranus
2. Clive Sinclair
3. Prime Minister of Canada, Pierre Trudeau
4. Liverpool
5. Glasgow
6. M5
7. Royal Opera House
8. Kenny Dalglish
9. Marc Bolan
10. Freddie Laker
11. The Sex Pistols
12. Guillotine
13. Steve Biko
14. Brit Awards
15. Smallpox
16. Fire Service
17. Peter Phillips (son of Princess Anne)
18. Heathrow's terminals
19. The Morecambe & Wise Christmas Show
20. Star Wars

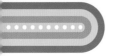 

Answers

The Year That Was – 1978

1. Anna Ford
2. The Hitchhiker's Guide to the Galaxy
3. Saatchi & Saatchi
4. Naturist beach
5. Nottingham Forest
6. Sail around the world single-handedly
7. Garfield
8. Ian Botham
9. Evita
10. Argentina
11. Louise Brown
12. English Channel/ The Channel
13. He was stabbed with a poison-tipped umbrella.
14. Liverpool
15. Viv Anderson
16. The Times
17. Concrete Cows
18. Chlorofluorocarbons (CFCs) in aerosol products
19. Grease
20. 1st May

The Year That Was – 1979

1. The Winter of Discontent
2. Sid Vicious
3. Trevor Francis
4. Snow
5. Three Mile Island
6. One
7. Airey Neave
8. Swamp rabbit
9. Jeremy Thorpe
10. The Happy Meal
11. He cut it by 23 percentage points to 60 per cent.
12. Skylab
13. Sebastian Coe
14. Fastnet Yacht Race
15. Saturn
16. To the Manor Born
17. Astra
18. Oil
19. Afghanistan
20. His native Poland

70s Sitcoms

1. George & Mildred
2. The Cuckoo Waltz
3. Rising Damp
4. Sykes
5. The Liver Birds
6. It Ain't Half Hot Mum
7. Are You Being Served?
8. Citizen Smith
9. On The Buses
10. Open All Hours
11. Man About The House
12. Some Mothers Do 'Ave 'Em
13. The Fall And Rise Of Reginald Perrin
14. Butterflies
15. Two's Company
16. Happy Ever After
17. Please Sir!
18. Dad's Army
19. Oh No It's Selwyn Froggitt
20. Whatever Happened To The Likely Lads?

Advertising

1. Terry Scott
2. Milk
3. Kenny Everett
4. Whizzer and Chips
5. Brut33
6. Texan bar
7. Pacers
8. Topic
9. Banana
10. Joan Collins
11. Soda Stream
12. Angel Delight
13. '...cigar called Hamlet'
14. Campari
15. Milk Tray
16. Milky Bar
17. Nimble bread
18. Hovis bread
19. Ridley Scott
20. Coca-Cola

Answers

Seventies Sport 1

1. Joe Frazier beat Muhammad Ali
2. West Germany
3. Arsenal
4. ODI – One Day International
5. He was the first person to sail non-stop west, against the prevailing winds.
6. Bobby Fischer
7. It was South Africa's last Test match for 22 years.
8. The Thrilla in Manila
9. Pat Darcy
10. 1978
11. Czechoslovakia
12. 1977
13. Olga Korbut
14. Geoff Capes
15. Queen Elizabeth II
16. David Hemery
17. John Conteh
18. Willis Reed
19. Mary Peters
20. Secretariat

Toys and Games

1. Troll Doll
2. Readicut
3. Rock'em Sock'em Robots
4. Speak and Spell
5. Mastermind
6. Red
7. Etch a Sketch
8. Spirograph
9. Katy Copycat
10. Frustration
11. Buccaneer
12. Operation
13. Mousetrap
14. Subbuteo (Falco subbuteo)
15. Bigtrak
16. Action Man
17. The Spacehopper
18. Stock Car Smash Up
19. Perfection
20. Merlin

Seventies Cars

1. Cortina
2. Ford Escort
3. Austin Marina
4. The Mini
5. Vauxhall Viva
6. Hillman Imp
7. Austin Allegro
8. Ford Granada (early models aka Ford Consul)
9. Lotus Esprit
10. Ford Capri
11. Varnished wooden (Ash) frame
12. Hillman Avenger
13. Bedford
14. Rolls Royce Phantom VI
15. 1974
16. Austin 1100
17. Hillman Imp
18. Lamborghini Countach
19. Lotus Esprit
20. Aston Martin Lagonda
Countryman

Children's Television Programmes

1. Screen Test
2. Noah & Nelly
3. Claptrap Von Spilldebeans
4. Wacky Races
5. Camberwick Green
6. Statler Hilton and the Waldorf-Astoria
7. The Magic Round-about
8. Bob Carolgees
9. Herbie
10. Cook
11. Birmingham
12. Petra
13. Joe 90
14. The Clangers
15. Dog, cat, frog
16. The Banana Splits
17. Comedian Mike Reid
18. Trumpton
19. Why Don't You Just Switch Off Your Television Set and Go Out and Do Something Less Boring Instead?
20. Bagpuss

Seventies Fashion

1. Wrap dress
2. Roy Halston
3. Biba
4. Laura Ashley
5. Farrah Fawcett-Majors
6. The stage outfits were tax-deductible if they couldn't be worn as normal street clothes.
7. Denim
8. Sonia Rykiel
9. Vivienne Westwood
10. Yves St Laurent
11. Ali Macgraw
12. Marie Helvin
13. Stevie Nicks
14. Ziggy Stardust
15. Lauren Hutton
16. Black
17. Giorgio Armani
18. Missoni
19. Malcolm McLaren
20. Iman

Monty Python's Flying Circus

1. 'The Liberty Bell' by John Philip Sousa
2. Red Leicester
3. One pound
4. Being hit on the head lessons
5. Lobster Thermidor
6. Surprise
7. Jump across the English Channel
8. Terry Gilliam and Terry Jones
9. Biggus Dickus
10. Heidegger
11. The Monty Python Matching Tie and Handkerchief
12. Pink Floyd and Led Zeppelin
13. George Harrison
14. The Dead Parrot Sketch
15. Eric Idle and Terry Jones
16. Bevis
17. Monty Python's Big Red Book
18. Eric
19. '...completely different.'
20. The Larch

Name the Actor in Both Films

1. Robert Duvall
2. Harrison Ford
3. Roy Scheider
4. Ryan O'Neal
5. Peter Fonda
6. Clint Eastwood
7. Michael York
8. Sylvester Stallone
9. James Caan
10. John Travolta
11. Jeff Bridges
12. Al Pacino
13. Burt Reynolds
14. Dustin Hoffman
15. Donald Sutherland
16. Jack Nicholson
17. John Hurt
18. Robert De Niro
19. Sean Connery
20. Robert Redford
21. Christopher Walken
22. Martin Sheen
23. Robert Shaw
24. Gene Hackman
25. Woody Allen
26. Marlon Brando
27. Elliot Gould
28. Richard Dreyfuss
29. Gene Wilder
30. Michael Caine

Robert De Niro

1. 1943
2. That he was gay
3. Bobby Milk
4. Cowardly Lion
5. Stella Adler
6. Shelley Winters
7. Hi, Mom!
8. Mean Streets, Taxi Driver and New York, New York
9. Baseball
10. Taxi Driver
11. Diahnne Abbott
12. Sonny Corleone
13. Vito Corleone
14. The Deer Hunter
15. Taxi Driver
16. Spat in his face
17. 'You talkin' to me?'
18. New York, New York
19. Harvey Keitel
20. Bernard Herrmann

Answers

Science

1. Digital watch
2. 1970
3. microprocessor
4. Enterprise
5. Ronald Wayne
6. Supercomputer
7. Polaroid
8. Betamax
9. Word processor – the IBM Magnetic Tape/Selectric Typewriter (IBM MT/ST)
10. 1970
11. @
12. Smallpox
13. Home video game console
14. Pong
15. Gaia hypothesis
16. Hewlett-Packard
17. Mercury
18. Jupiter
19. Search for Extraterrestrial Intelligence
20. Westworld

Books of the Seventies – Science-fiction

1. Ringworld
2. Time and Again
3. The Lathe of Heaven
4. Dragonquest
5. The Gods Themselves
6. The Stepford Wives
7. What Entropy Means To Me
8. Gravity's Rainbow
9. Rendezvous with Rama
10. The Man Who Folded Himself
11. The Mote in God's Eye
12. The Dispossessed
13. The Forever War
14. Children of Dune
15. A Scanner Darkly
16. Gateway
17. The Hitchhiker's Guide to the Galaxy
18. The Fountains of Paradise
19. Kindred
20. Titan

Opening Lines – Name That Tune

1. 'Teenage Kicks' (The Undertones)
2. 'Heart Of Glass' (Blondie)
3. 'Band On The Run' (Wings)
4. 'Life On Mars' (David Bowie)
5. 'Psycho Killer' (Talking Heads)
6. 'Born To Run' (Bruce Springsteen)
7. 'Let's Get It On' (Marvin Gaye)
8. 'God Save The Queen' (Sex Pistols)
9. 'Transmission' (Joy Division)
10. 'Don't Stop 'Til You Get Enough' (Michael Jackson)
11. 'Blitzkrieg Bop' (The Ramones)
12. 'Stairway To Heaven' (Led Zeppelin)
13. 'Go Your Own Way' (Fleetwood Mac)
14. 'Superstition' (Stevie Wonder)
15. 'Are 'Friends' Electric?' (Tubeway Army)
16. 'London Calling' (The Clash)
17. 'Comfortably Numb' (Pink Floyd)
18. 'Highway To Hell' (AC/DC)
19. 'I Feel Love' (Donna Summer)
20. 'Heroes' (David Bowie)

More Television

1. Dave Allen
2. The Duchess of Duke Street
3. Tomsk
4. Vision On and Take Hart
5. 'And this is me.'
6. Black Beauty
7. Kunta Kinte
8. Ronnie Barker
9. Purdey
10. 'Ooh, you are awful but I like you!'
11. The Benny Hill Show
12. Dad's Army
13. The Onedin Line
14. Charlie's Angels: he voiced the unseen millionaire, Charles Townsend, who gave them their assignment each week via speakerphone.
15. 1974
16. Paint Along With Nancy
17. Starsky and Hutch
18. Some Mothers Do 'Ave 'Em
19. It's a Knockout
20. Frank Bough

Answers

Seventies Sport 2

1. Evonne Goolagong
2. Leeds United
3. Martin Peters
4. Liverpool
5. Harvey Smith
6. Nadia Comăneci
7. Björn Borg
8. Kevin Keegan
9. Seven
10. Jimmy Connors
11. Giant Haystacks and Big Daddy
12. John McEnroe
13. Brian Jacks
14. Leon Spinks
15. Black September
16. Kent
17. Eddy Merckx
18. Nijinsky II
19. Roberto Clemente
20. James Hunt

Elizabeth II and the Silver Jubilee

1. 6th February 1977
2. False. They visited 36 counties.
3. The Royal Train
4. Windsor Castle
5. St Paul's Cathedral
6. The Mall
7. Silver Ghost Rolls Royce cars
8. 500 million
9. 7th June
10. 9th June
11. Elizabeth I
12. River Progress
13. Silver Jubilee Walkway and the South Bank Jubilee Gardens
14. 'I Don't Want to Talk About It'
15. Tower Bridge
16. HMY Britannia
17. Paul Fitzgerald
18. True
19. Derby
20. 25 pence

Seventies Sitcoms

1. Fletcher
2. Grace Brothers
3. Dentist
4. Oh No, It's Selwyn Froggitt!
5. Please Sir!
6. It featured a man sharing a flat with two women.
7. Thelma
8. Shut up!
9. Blake or 'Blakey'
10. You're Only Young Twice
11. Hattie Jacques died of a heart attack.
12. Lewis Collins
13. Nurse Gladys Emmanuel
14. George & Mildred
15. The Tooting Popular Front
16. Hippopotamus
17. Dad's Army
18. Steptoe and Son
19. Vienna
20. Jessica

Star Wars

1. Luke Starkiller
2. Merchandising rights
3. Yoda
4. C-3PO
5. R2D2
6. Millennium Falcon
7. Chewbacca
8. True
9. All of them
10. Never
11. Reel 2 Dialogue Track 2 (editor's shorthand for cans of film on American Graffiti)
12. $10,000
13. Tatooine
14. A hamburger with an olive on the side
15. Zulu
16. Irvin Kershner
17. Chewbacca
18. Alec Guinness
19. Orson Welles
20. Alec Guinness

Answers

Seventies Fads and Crazes

1. Raleigh Chopper
2. Frisbee
3. Weebles
4. Israeli
5. Erich von Däniken
6. Spokey Dokeys
7. Cat's Cradle
8. French skipping
9. Space Hopper
10. Argos
11. Atlantic Ocean
12. 'Bye, Bye, Baby'
13. View-Master
14. Pet Rock
15. Stylophone
16. Kirsch
17. Herbie
18. Jimmy Osmond
19. Chicken Kiev
20. Henry 'The Fonz' Winkler

Meryl Streep

1. 1949
2. New Jersey
3. Yale
4. Sigourney Weaver
5. Tony Award
6. Taxi Driver
7. King Kong
8. Julia
9. Robert De Niro
10. John Cazale
11. Holocaust
12. Kate Jackson
13. François Truffaut
14. Manhattan
15. The Deer Hunter
16. Kramer vs. Kramer
17. Alan Alda
18. Katharine Hepburn
19. Bette Davis
20. Nineteen

Fawlty Towers

1. Torquay
2. Twelve
3. He was the proprietor of the Gleneagles Hotel in Torquay – the inspiration for Basil Fawlty.
4. Connie Booth
5. O'Reilly
6. Geoffrey Palmer
7. Ken Campbell
8. Red
9. Kurt
10. Korean War
11. Four
12. Basil
13. The Major
14. Miss Abitha Tibbs and Miss Ursula Gatsby
15. It was the name of the country club in Bourne End, Buckinghamshire that was used for exterior shots of Fawlty Towers.
16. 'Basil the Rat'
17. Bernard Cribbins
18. Dragonfly
19. Lord Melbury
20. Duck without oranges or cherries
21. In the second series he named the guest who was caught in his room with a blow up doll, Mr Ingrams.

Grease

1. 1958
2. Rydell High
3. Marie Osmond
4. Olsson
5. Jeff Conaway (Kenickie)
6. The Teen Angel (Frankie Avalon)
7. Twenty-three
8. Twenty-eight
9. Olivia Newton-John
10. Rebel Without a Cause
11. '...athletic supporter'
12. Stagnant water near the bridge
13. '...pink'
14. Combed their hair
15. Hallmark card
16. 'You're The One That I Want'
17. Frenchy
18. Burger Palace Boys
19. 'Hopelessly Devoted to You'
20. Two of a Kind

Answers

Name the Actress in Both Films

1. Cybill Shepherd
2. Faye Dunaway
3. Julie Christie
4. Jacqueline Bisset
5. Olivia Newton-John
6. Mia Farrow
7. Raquel Welch
8. Jane Fonda
9. Barbra Streisand
10. Goldie Hawn
11. Meryl Streep
12. Catherine Deneuve
13. Candice Bergen
14. Ellen Burstyn
15. Teri Garr
16. Sissy Spacek
17. Jodie Foster
18. Shelley Duvall
19. Diane Keaton
20. Joanne Woodward
21. Pam Grier
22. Sigourney Weaver
23. Jane Seymour
24. Glenda Jackson
25. Farrah Fawcett
26. Carrie Fisher
27. Ali McGraw
28. Jessica Lange
29. Vanessa Redgrave
30. Ursula Andress

More Science

1. Stephen Hawking
2. True
3. Henry Heimlich
4. Lucy
5. Nuclear test explosion
6. Barcode scanning
7. Rubik's Cube
8. Aryabhata
9. Viking 1
10. Microcomputer
11. The Altair 8800
12. Lyme disease
13. A face
14. The Selfish Gene
15. Word processing
16. Created the first complete genome sequence
17. Atari 2600 (or Atari VCS)
18. Stealth plane
19. Wernher von Braun – inventor of Hitler's V2
20. VisiCalc

Name the Novelist – Books

1. Anne Rice
2. Stephen King
3. Colleen McCullough
4. Alex Haley
5. John Irving
6. Stephen King
7. James Herriot
8. William Peter Blatty
9. William Styron
10. Kurt Vonnegut
11. John le Carré
12. Robert M. Pirsig
13. Carl Bernstein
14. Helene Hanff
15. Frederick Forsyth
16. Norman Miller
17. James Dickey
18. John le Carré
19. Eric Segal
20. John Updike
21. Richard Adams
22. William Goldman
23. James Clavell
24. Erica Jong
25. Thomas Pynchon
26. Jeffrey Archer
27. Iris Murdoch
28. Tom Wolfe
29. John Fowles
30. Nadine Gordimer

Advertising 2

1. Derek Nimmo
2. Rise and Shine
3. Cadbury Fudge
4. Toffo
5. Cresta
6. False. It's an urban myth.
7. 2½ pence
8. Murray Walker
9. Rich Tea biscuit
10. Corona
11. Kellogg's Special K
12. Persil
13. Harp
14. Dulux paint (he was the Dulux dog)
15. Frank Muir
16. Pepsi
17. Harmony hairspray
18. Quavers
19. Fisher Price
20. Ford

Answers

Rocky

1. 1976
2. Three
3. True
4. Ken Norton
5. Carl Weathers (Apollo Creed)
6. Twenty-eight days
7. Susan Sarandon
8. Talia Shire
9. In a pet shop
10. Mickey
11. Butkus
12. Philadelphia Art Museum
13. He directed the film
14. Shamrock Meats
15. False
16. True
17. Francis Ford Coppola
18. False. He lived at 1818 East Tusculum Street, Philadelphia PA 19134.
19. Charlie Chaplin
20. True

Seventies Blockbusters

1. Oliver's Story
2. Ernst Stavro Blofeld
3. The Godfather
4. George Lucas
5. Marlon Brando
6. Schlitz beer (the world's largest beer company during the 1930s)
7. Blazing Saddles
8. The Towering Inferno
9. Kirk Douglas
10. Mick Jagger
11. Orca
12. Chuck Wepner
13. 2001 Odyssey
14. That Darth Vader is Luke's father
15. Steve McQueen
16. Frog
17. John 'Bluto' Blutarsky
18. Never
19. Superman
20. Billy

More Children's Television

1. Roobarb and Custard
2. John Craven's Newsround
3. Purple
4. Mysterons
5. Richard Baker
6. Magpie
7. Cookie Monster
8. The Harlem Globe-trotters
9. Nine
10. Space 1999
11. Hong Kong Phooey
12. How!
13. Mr Benn
14. The Tomorrow People
15. Originally there was one, but when it was stolen in the mid-1970s it was replaced by Big Ted and Little Ted
16. White Horses
17. Play Away
18. Rentaghost
19. The Six Million Dollar Man
20. Officer Dibble

Jaws

1. Peter Benchley
2. All of them
3. Duel
4. Chrissie, the shark's first victim.
5. Three
6. $471 million
7. Martha's Vineyard
8. Robert Duvall
9. Hooper (Richard Dreyfus)
10. Lee Marvin
11. Roy Scheider (Brody)
12. Richard Dreyfuss
13. John Williams
14. He laughed, thinking it was a joke, because it was so simple.
15. '...dorsal...tail'
16. His lawyer, Bruce Ramer
17. Mayor of Amity
18. HELP!!! SHARK
19. Water level
20. Charlton Heston

Answers

Here Today, Gone Tomorrow

1. 'Billy Don't Be a Hero'
2. 1977
3. Mungo Jerry
4. 'Grandad'
5. Wizzard
6. Clare
7. 'Snoopy vs. the Red Baron'
8. 'Whispering Grass'
9. January
10. He spoke every word.
11. Jasper Carrott
12. Dutch
13. Demis Roussos
14. 'Convoy'
15. Jimmy
16. 1978
17. 'Rivers Of Babylon'
18. 'Save Your Kisses For Me', 'Angelo' and 'Figaro'
19. 'Don't Give Up on Us'
20. 'Annie's Song'

Al Pacino

1. 1940
2. Alfredo
3. Sonny
4. To become a basketball player
5. Lee Strasberg
6. Heroin addiction
7. Jim Morrison
8. Gene Hackman
9. Dog Day Afternoon
10. Michael Corleone
11. Serpico (1974) and Dog Day Afternoon (1976)
12. Diane Keaton
13. He was angry at being nominated for Best Supporting Actor in The Godfather, when he had more screen time than Best Actor winner, Marlon Brando.
14. Marathon Man
15. Tony Award
16. Bobby Deerfield
17. Close Encounters of the Third Kind
18. Serpico
19. . . . And Justice for All
20. Apocalypse Now

Top of the Pops

1. Carl Douglas
2. 1975
3. The Jackson Five
4. 'We Don't Talk Anymore'
5. 'Tie a Yellow Ribbon Round the Ole Oak Tree'
6. 'Imagine'
7. 1977
8. Off the Wall
9. Ian Dury & The Blockheads
10. Eighteen
11. London Calling by The Clash
12. 'Bright Eyes'
13. Leo Sayer
14. Tina Charles
15. 'Seasons in the Sun'
16. 'The Name of the Game'
17. Mud
18. 'Jealous Mind'
19. The New Seekers
20. The Spy Who Loved Me

Famous TV Catchphrases

1. Mork & Mindy
2. The Waltons
3. Fantasy Island
4. The Incredible Hulk
5. Are you Being Served?
6. Wacky Races
7. The Dick Emery Show
8. The Muppet Show
9. Scooby-Doo, Where Are You!
10. Charlie's Angels
11. The Two Ronnies
12. Some Mothers Do 'Ave 'Em
13. Monty Python's Flying Circus
14. Are You Being Served?
15. Dad's Army
16. Steptoe & Son
17. The Good Life
18. Citizen Smith
19. The Dick Emery Show
20. It Ain't Half Hot Mum
21. The Fall And Rise Of Reginald Perrin
22. The Generation Game
23. Love Thy Neighbour
24. Mastermind
25. Nearest & Dearest
26. Monty Python's Flying Circus
27. Morecambe and Wise
28. The Basil Brush Show
29. The Sweeney
30. The Addams Family

Answers

Opening Lines – Name That Tune

1. 'I Will Survive' (Gloria Gaynor)
2. 'Maggie May' (Rod Stewart)
3. 'Let's Stay Together' (Al Green)
4. 'Yes Sir, I Can Boogie' (Baccara)
5. 'Dancing Queen' (ABBA)
6. 'Mandy' (Barry Manilow)
7. 'Get It On' (T. Rex)
8. 'Paranoid' (Black Sabbath)
9. 'Knock On Wood' (Amii Stewart)
10. 'Killing Me Softly' (Roberta Flack)
11. 'Walk On The Wild Side' (Lou Reed)
12. 'Midnight Train To Georgia' (Gladys Knight And The Pips)
13. 'Smoke On The Water' (Deep Purple)
14. 'What's Going On' (Marvin Gaye)
15. 'Stayin' Alive' (Bee Gees)
16. Shang-A-Lang (Bay City Rollers)
17. 'Rock Lobster' (The B52's)
18. 'Y.M.C.A.' (Village People)
19. 'The Eton Rifles' (The Jam)
20. 'My Sharona' (The Knack)

Close Encounters of the Third Kind

1. 1973
2. 1977
3. Sonora Desert
4. Electrical lineman
5. Teri Garr
6. The actual house that was purchased to be the Neary's house. It was sold again after the filming.
7. False. It was Jack Nicholson.
8. François Truffaut
9. 'Are we the first?'
10. John Williams
11. Melinda Dillon
12. Wyoming
13. Computer-generated imagery (CGI)
14. Boarded the mothership
15. Douglas Trumbull
16. R2D2 from Star Wars
17. Star Wars
18. The Searchers
19. George Lucas, Star Wars
20. Eight

Even More Children's Television

1. 3 and 4 respectively
2. Belle and Sebastian
3. Una Stubbs
4. A cigarette in a yellow holder
5. Skydiving with her boyfriend, Steve Austin
6. The van in Scooby-Doo, Where Are You!
7. The Goodies
8. The Flintstones
9. Fingerbobs
10. Dottie
11. Go With Noakes
12. Deputy Dawg
13. Spinning
14. Emu's Broadcasting Company (1975–1980)
15. Fred
16. 1978
17. Ragtime
18. Here Come the Double Deckers
19. Pixie and Dixie were grey mice (or 'meeces' as Mr Jinks the cat called them)
20. Wait Till Your Father Gets Home

Barbra Streisand

1. 1942
2. Barbara Streisand
3. Brooklyn
4. Acting
5. Bobby Fischer
6. The Owl and the Pussycat
7. Capricorn One
8. Elliott Gould
9. Canada. She dated Prime Minister Pierre Trudeau, but turned down his marriage proposal.
10. What's Up, Doc?
11. A Star Is Born
12. Richard Nixon
13. Robert Redford
14. No More Tears (Enough Is Enough)
15. Kris Kristofferson
16. Elvis Presley
17. 'You Don't Bring Me Flowers'
18. Forty-two
19. Mike Nichols
20. 'Mother of All Contemporary Pop Divas'

Answers

Iconic Film Quotations – Name the Film

1. Animal House
2. Dirty Harry
3. Close Encounters of the Third Kind
4. Marathon Man
5. Diamonds Are Forever
6. Grease
7. All the President's Men
8. Rocky
9. Taxi Driver
10. Jaws
11. One Flew over the Cuckoo's Nest
12. Cabaret
13. Last Tango in Paris
14. Superman
15. The Deer Hunter
16. The Exorcist
17. Monty Python and the Holy Grail
18. The Godfather
19. Apocalypse Now
20. The Rocky Horror Picture Show

Seventies Children's Books

1. Watership Down, Richard Adams
2. The Princess Bride, William Goldman
3. The Lorax, Dr Seuss
4. Bridge to Terabithia, Katharine Paterson
5. The Neverending Story, Michael Ende
6. Mrs Frisby and the Rats of Nimh, Robert C. O'Brien
7. Fantastic Mr Fox, Roald Dahl
8. Charlie and the Great Glass Elevator, Roald Dahl
9. The Dark is Rising, Susan Cooper
10. Are You There, God? It's Me, Margaret, Judy Blume
11. Cloudy With a Chance of Meatballs, Judi Barrett
12. Danny the Champion of the World, Roald Dahl
13. Carrie's War, Nina Bawden
14. A Bear Called Paddington, Michael Bond
15. When Hitler Stole Pink Rabbit, Judith Kerr
16. Flambards, K.M. Peyton
17. Dogger, Shirley Hughes
18. The Chocolate War, Robert Cormier
19. I'm the King of the Castle, Susan Hill
20. Meg and Mog, Helen Nicoll

Game and Quiz Shows

1. Ask the Family
2. Jimmy Tarbuck
3. They answered each question with the name of a Marxist.
4. Sale of the Century
5. Patrick Campbell
6. Runaround
7. Nigel Rees
8. Tom O'Connor
9. The Golden Shot
10. The Krypton Factor
11. Whodunnit?
12. Mastermind
13. Garbage
14. Bruce Forsyth and the Generation Game
15. Screen Test
16. Mr & Mrs
17. A Question of Sport
18. Michael Aspel
19. Face The Music
20. Michael Aspel

Answers

The Good Life

1. He was a draughtsman in a company that made plastic toys for cereal packets
2. 'Somewhere Over the Rainbow'
3. Talking to plants
4. Animal dung
5. Tom's old boss, Andrew
6. Spinning wheel
7. Lenin
8. Leeks
9. Peapods
10. She was secretly attending a slimming club
11. Miss Dollie Mountshaft
12. Maria
13. Stinging nettles
14. Pinky and Perky
15. Tom and Barbara's goat
16. Surplus vegetables
17. Pottery
18. Windbreak
19. Margo complained about the noise.
20. Barbara's runner bean during the talking to plants experiment

Farrah Fawcett

1. 1947
2. Ferrah Fawcett
3. Texas
4. 'Most Beautiful Student'
5. Initially she studied Microbiology then switched to Art.
6. The Partridge Family
7. Lee Majors
8. 1982
9. Jill Munroe
10. Kate Jackson and Jaclyn Smith
11. John Bosley
12. Townsend Associates
13. Posters
14. Goldie Hawn
15. The Six Million Dollar Man
16. Ryan O'Neal
17. She caught him in bed with a younger woman.
18. Ryan O'Neal
19. Ryan O'Neal's
20. Six

Seventies Sport 3

1. George Foreman
2. Derby County
3. Streaker
4. George Foreman
5. Sunderland
6. Sonny Liston
7. Barry Sheene
8. £13,500
9. Everton
10. Robert Craig 'Evel' Knievel
11. Hank Aaron
12. Jackie Stewart
13. 1970
14. O.J. Simpson
15. Gerd Müller
16. Ajax
17. Gordon Banks
18. Sugar Ray Leonard
19. Keegan
20. Wales